Legends of Paul Bunyan

Pecos Bill: Texas Cowpuncher

John Henry and His Hammer

Fire-Fightin' Mose

Other books by Harold W. Felton

Bowleg Bill: Seagoing Cowpuncher

Cowboy Jamboree: Western Songs and Lore

New Tall Tales of Pecos Bill

Mike Fink: Best of the Keelboatmen

Illustrated by Leonard Everett Fisher

By Harold W. Felton

The World's Most Truthful Man

TALL TALES TOLD BY ED GRANT IN MAINE

Grant

DODD, MEAD & COMPANY
NEW YORK

J 398.2

1158504

To Richie

Contents

CONTENTS

A Word from the Author

The legend of Rangeley, Maine, is Ed Grant. He became so because he could tell a tall tale so that it stayed told. He told of things that probably couldn't have happened in such a fashion that it seemed as if they had.

Uncle Ed, as he was known, used to say, "The best fun you have is the fun you make yourself." He also

9

said, "I could talk until the sun goes down and the moon comes up." He loved to talk and he loved to make his own fun. Little wonder the tales he told still echo endlessly around the hearthstones, the kitchen stoves, and the hot-air registers in the Maine woods region where he lived.

Edward Grant was born at Whitefield, Maine, in 1839. He died in Rangeley in 1919. He went to Rangeley in 1865 and ran trap lines north to the Canadian border. He became a hunting and fishing guide in 1869. In 1878, he built the Kennebago Hotel, and eight years later he built the camps at Beaver Pond, a source of delight for summer visitors and sportsmen. A particular delight was the stories with which Ed Grant entertained his guests.

"The Tame Trout" found its way into print in the early 1890's through Francis I. Maule, an advertising man from Philadelphia who had fallen under the spell of the Sage of Beaver Pond and his tales. It reached me through Ben Botkin's *Treasury of New England Folklore*. There was something about that story. It stayed with me. I was certain that tale, and others, were still alive at its birthplace.

A few years later and a few letters later, I was in Rangeley, and I was right. A man who could tell such a tale told others and they were still there, waiting to be put into print, waiting for someone to come and let them be heard again and to let them be read.

A WORD FROM THE AUTHOR

Hall Grant, Ed's son, told the stories to me. So did Herbert Welch. Ed Grant and his tales were fresh in their minds, as if forty, sixty, or even seventy years and more had not sped by. Sid Harden remembered some of them. Harold McCard, Frank Porter, Mason Russell, Maitland G. Barter, Prudence Richardson, and Harland Curtis gave me their memories, as did Gordon Cushman, who was Ed's grandson.

Hall Grant and Herbert Welch both showed more than a little of the story-teller's art, relating the tales with fine embellishment and gesture, and with a serious purpose — to entertain. I asked Hall Grant if there was a tall tale club around Rangeley and the lake area. All Maine guides can tell tall tales. Ed Grant was the acknowledged master. It seemed to me that in such a community, a tall tale club would not only be possible, but probable.

"Tall tale club?" he queried.

"Yes. You know. A liar's club. They have them in other places."

"Oh, no," he replied. "We couldn't do that here. There ain't no liars around here."

I knew I had caught a glimpse of the art of Ed Grant.

I talked to Will Grant, Ed's elder son, and his wife, Lena Robbins Grant. She had written down some of the tales and they were published in the *Boston Post* in 1920. Kathleen Ross and Ann True of the younger generation at Rangeley High School knew some of the

stories and wrote them down for me. Hall Grant gave
me an ancient typed copy of "The Tame Trout" and
a number of other tales. Hartry H. Field of Phillips
had caused the Maule booklet to be reprinted.

Stories of Paul Bunyan were in the woods in Ed
Grant's time. Sid Harden and Hall Grant both heard
them in the Maine woods in the 1880's. They heard
them while working in lumber camps, and Hall had
heard tales of the mighty logger at his father's hotel.

Uncle Ed had the friendship, attention, and respect
of a great many good and prominent people. A Maine
guide lives with, teaches, and helps leaders in the
business, social, political, financial, educational, and
many other worlds. So does the operator of Maine
camps. People who like to hunt and fish seek out the
services of a man who knows the strange world of
woods, lake and stream; and long days in the woods or
on the water and nights around the campfire create
enduring and firm friendships.

It is a great mistake to think that because a guide
is a woodsman, he is a backwoodsman; that because he
dresses in rough clothes, he is a rough character and
unsophisticated. If the sportsman learns where and
how to hunt and fish, his guide is learning something,
too, of the world from which his guest came. If he
seems rustic, one should not be confused. A Maine
twang in the voice, a battered hat with trout flies in

the band, Maine words and sounds on the tip of the tongue may be there because visitors expect them to be there. But they are part of a Maine man's heritage, and Maine words are good, and a battered hat is comfortable, and where is a better place to carry trout flies?

Many of my Rangeley friends recalled the "Beaver Terror," invented by the Sage of Beaver Pond. It was a fish lure, a masterpiece that varied in its construction from time to time, but which was ordinarily made of a hawk's wing, a scrap of beaver fur, some bright feathers, perhaps a civet cat's tail, and a suitable dash of red flannel, all artistically covering a hook the size of a hay hook. Obviously, it was appropriate for a fish the size of those in the Beaver Pond area, and especially suitable to hook securely the "big one that got away." The great invention was a sure solace and a great comfort to the fisherman who came to camp with a story of how the big one was clever enough to escape capture. It was a joy to the man who had been successful.

Ed Grant knew the "receipt" for building tall tales. It would be something like this:

Take a good solid fact. A small one will do, but it should be a lively one. Rub it until it shines, and place the fact so that it squares with the compass. This should be done carefully, as a mispointed fact will ruin the result. Weave as tall a tale as may be desired,

13

and put it on top of the shining fact. Keep the tale tall and pointed. A very tall tale may be balanced on a very small fact.

The tales in the following pages are those told to me in Rangeley. I can read or hear some stories and forget them. Some I cannot, and these belong to the latter class. It has happened to me before, and I knew what the end would be. I would have to do a book.

— *Harold W. Felton*

Meet Ed Grant

It happened in Maine, in Rangeley, on the Kennebago River. It happened at Beaver Pond. But it might
have happened anywhere else, because tall tales are
told everywhere. The difference is that Ed Grant told
them in Maine, there at Rangeley and at Beaver Pond,
and the tales he told stayed told.

Men have stretched the blanket, and drawn the

long bow — that is to say, they have told tall tales — in all the years and in all places. They are told. They create a smile, or a laugh. They are forgotten and they are remembered. A good story does not disappear. It stays, and it lives. How long it lives depends on who tells it. Ed Grant's stories have lived a long time. He was a master storyteller, and his stories stuck.

Naturally, Ed Grant was born in Maine, a true State o' Mainer. He went to Rangeley when he was still a young man and ran trap lines to the Canadian border. He and John Meader were partners, and later Rufe Crosby became his trapping partner.

It was not long before Ed became a guide. A Maine guide is also a cook, and a good one. An important part of his job is to keep his party well fed and dry and comfortable, besides finding good fishing and hunting. Ed Grant turned to the great work of supplying food and shelter for the sportsmen and vacationers who sought this land that is a fisherman's delight and a hunter's paradise. At Beaver Pond his tall tales came into flower. It was there that his charm and wit and his story-telling skill held his small audience eager captive.

Those who wonder why the Maine coast is said to be "down east" instead of "up north" should remember that in Maine language a "camp" is a cabin. Summer visitors came to Ed Grant's camps, and they came back. They came for good food and good shelter, and the blue water and blue sky, white puffy clouds, the green of Maine forests, the fishing and the hunting, the summer Maine weather, and for the tall tales. Lots of them came back for the tall tales. Ed Grant became Uncle Ed. The Sage of Beaver Pond. The "world's most truthful man."

Uncle Ed circulated among his guests and told his tales. A tall tale can be told anywhere. On the porch with the beautiful Maine world in plain view. In the big room next to the dining room, on chilly nights and rainy days before a crackling blaze. In a boat. On the trail. All the Sage of Beaver Pond needed was an appropriate time and an audience. A little prompting. A slight encouragement. A question. "Wal, sir, seein' it's you, I'll tell you," he would say, and then the story would unfold.

There was the visitor who asked about danger in the boat on the pond.

"This here feller was kinda touchy 'bout a boat," Uncle Ed recalled. "Nervous as a long-tailed cat in a roomful of rockin' chairs, he was. Always wonderin' if it was safe.

"So I told him not to worry. I told him, an' 'course it was the truth, that I knew every rock in the pond.

"Wal, sir, I was rowin' along, an' all of a sudden, the boat hit a rock, Rubbed against it, y'know?

"That feller was skeered, I kin tell you. He grabbed the edges of the boat with both hands. Tight. Held on so hard his knuckles got white. He give me a skeered look. Reproachful, y'know? An' he says, in a screamin' kind of voice, he says, 'I thought you knowed every rock in this pond?'

" 'Yup,' I sez. 'I do. That's one of 'em right there,' I says. I didn't change my stroke or nothin'. Kep' right on rowin', jest's if nothin' happened."

Ed Grant was a tall man, about six feet, and thin. He wore a mustache, until he grew a beard in his early seventies. His pipe looms large in the recollections of all those who heard the tales told by the master. It was his indispensable prop. He would take it out, rub it, pack it, tamp it, shape the load, light a match, fail to touch it to the pipe, light another, and another, hold it in mid-air without touching it to the load, light the pipe at last, permit it to go out, light it again.

The match died, or he blew it out just at the point where it seemed sure to burn his fingers. He tamped the ashes down better, better still, knocked the top ashes off, fussed with the bed, blew through it, tapped it out. All this was done in exactly the right way to heighten interest, permit a laugh, produce a dramatic effect, permit wonder, permit a question or forbid a question. When Uncle Ed was telling a story, he worked at it every minute of the time, without seeming to. It took a great many matches and very little tobacco.

There were many stories. Some of them may seem to stretch the imagination a bit. Just a little, of course. But Uncle Ed said, "I always like to make sure I don't tell no more than the precise exact truth."

Now you have met Ed Grant, and here are some of the tales he told in Maine.

Uncle Ed's Unusual Bear Hide

Uncle Ed built a number of camps on Beaver Pond.
Trout and landlocked salmon were a great attraction
for fishermen. The beautiful Seven Ponds District and
the coolness and quiet drew summer visitors. And of
all the attractions, not the least was Uncle Ed Grant.

The guests were gathered around the camp's fire
one evening when one of them said, "That's a beautiful bear skin, Uncle Ed."

"Yes, and a big one, too," another agreed. They were admiring the skin that was spread out on the wall at the side of the big fireplace.

"Yup. But it can't hold a candle to another one I got," Uncle Ed said.

"Where is that one? May we see it?"

"It's out to Rangeley jest now. I don't keep it here. Too valuable. Y'know bears is very important critters. We used to use the hides for bed coverin's, rugs, an' the like. Now most generally they hang 'em on walls.

"Wal, 'bout this here bear hide I was tellin' you 'bout. It was a big one, all right. But that warn't the most unusual thing 'bout it." Uncle Ed took out his pipe and began to pack down the tobacco in it. The guests knew they could count on a story.

"What was it that made the bear hide so unusual?" asked an eager listener.

"It didn't have no hole in it, an' that is what made it so unusual. Now a bear hide has almost got to have a hole in it. Where the bullet went, or several bullets, mebby. Or mebby even a knife. But this one didn't have no hole at all."

"Goodness, how could that be?"

The old man reached for a match. "Wal, seein' it's you, I'll tell you. We had this trap set 'longside a big spruce that had bin blowed down. Rufe Crosby was partners with me then, an' we was trappin' from Rangeley north to the Canadian border.

22

"We was tendin' our traps an' we come to this particular one. I was ahead, an' I see that we had captured a bear an' there he was in the trap. An' he was caught like I believe no other bear was ever caught.

" 'Hurry up, Rufe,' I yelled as soon as I see what I see, jest as I come 'round a bunch of hemlocks.

"Rufe come up an' says, 'Keerful. He don't look like he's caught in the trap. He's jest settin' there.'

"He was talkin' 'bout the bear I had seen. 'Nope,' I says. 'That bear is caught in the trap, all right, but in a most uncommon way.'

"An' he was, too, for he'd bin caught by the tail. Don't ask me how he done it, but it's a fact. There he was, with his tail in the trap.

"Rufe, he wanted to argue 'bout it. 'Why,' he says, 'no bear was ever caught by the tail. He'd have to be advancin' backwards, an' that ain't the way a bear advances.'

"But as sure as shootin', there the bear was. I never seen such a thing before, an' I don't ever expect to see such a thing agin. An' this bear was lookin' pretty sheepish, too.

"Rufe says, liftin' his gun, 'Let's put a bullet in him an' skin him.'

"But right then, I got an idee. 'No,' I says. 'I got an idee that might make that bear hide a most remarkable curiosity.'

"We was raisin' some sheep then, an' that is one

of the reasons we wanted to ketch this particular bear. He had bin killin' sheep. That mebby was one of the reasons the bear was settin' there lookin' so sheepish!

"We see that the bear had bin 'bout his sheep killin' agin, for there was seven dead sheep right there beside him, almost. The sheep warn't much damaged. He had jest that minute killed 'em. He must of backed into the trap while he was killin' 'em. So the first thing we done was to skin an' dress the sheep. After we got that done, we turned to Mister Bear. He was a-bellerin' now an' showin' his bad disposition with growls that shook the snow off of the hemlocks. He was a-shakin' with rage, stoppin' only ever' so often to look at his tail, like he was wonderin' why it wouldn't foller along after him. That bear was madder than a wet cat.

"I took a few pounds of sheep liver an' tied it to the end of a long pole.

" 'That's a long fishin' pole,' says Rufe. 'An' it's mighty funny bait.'

" 'This is a mighty funny fish,' I says, 'an' I don't want to git too close to it. Now you sneak over there back of them spruce an' git ready to shoot him if he gits away, or anything goes wrong.'

"Rufe done like I said, an' I moves up an' climbed up on the trunk of that dead spruce. Then I lowered the pole so the liver dangled jest in front of Mister Bear's nose.

"That got his attention an' took his mind off of his

tail. He was mad before, but now he got hungry with that liver danglin' there. He must of thought it was a snack descendin' from heaven.

"He made for the liver an' almost grabbed it with them hungry teeth. But I kep' the bait jest out of his reach.

"Wal, he warn't goin' to be cheated out of his snack like that, so he strained to git the liver, pullin' as hard as he could, an' 'course bein' held firm by the tail. He was a greedy one, I kin tell you. He grabbed, an' pulled, an' strained. It took a steady hand an' a steady eye, but I always was pretty good like that.

"He pulled so hard that fin'lly the skin give 'way round his nose, an' slipped back. If this done anything, it only made him hungrier an' madder. As he lunged an' pulled, his skin kep' breakin' away. 'Round his eyes, an' then his ears. Fin'lly his neck. Then his front legs. His shins started to show. Then he give a big plunge an' he walked right out of his skin, leavin' his pelt behind, held by the tail in the trap without a bullet hole or a knife mark in it.

" 'Git ready,' I yells to Rufe, 'cause this is the time I figgered there would be trouble.

" 'Right,' he says, liftin' his gun up.

"But when the bear reached the bait, his appetite was gone. He warn't hungry any more. He warn't mean, neither. Rufe didn't shoot, an' then, jest like the disposition of the bear had changed, my feelin's

25

started to change, too. Right away I felt sorry for that poor bear. An' he was bare, I kin tell you. He was a bare bear. Jest like Sampson lost his strength when he lost his hair, that bear had lost all his fight an' hunger. He stood there shiverin' an' helpless, an' he looked at me with such a sorrowful an' reproachful look that I wanted to do somethin' for him. Wanted to help him. An' I done it, too."

The old man tapped his pipe again and took out his big gold watch and held it out as far as its heavy chain would permit. After examining it critically for some time, he said, "But I ain't got time tonight. Some other time mebby I'll tell you 'bout that. Right now I think we all ought to git some sleep.

"But anyways that's how I got the bear hide with no hole in it. I always thought that was real curious, how that happened."

The Hideless Bear

"You told us you might tell us the story of what happened to the bear, Mr. Grant."

It was the next evening. After a day in the woods and on the water, the visitors at Beaver Pond were relaxing on the porch. The Maine scenery was as breathtaking as ever, but a bear hide with no hole in it naturally piqued curiosity about the bear.

"Which bear was that?" the Sage of Beaver Pond asked.

"The one that lost his skin."

"The one that was trapped and caught by his tail."

"Oh. That one. Wal, yup, there is more to that story, an' seein' it's you, I'll tell you 'bout it.

"Wal, I see this poor bear standin' bare, an' I felt sorry for him. I calls Rufe an' I says, 'We got to do somethin' for that bear.'

" 'What?' says Rufe. Rufe was a good trapper an' guide, but he didn't have too much 'magination.

" 'Come on,' I says. 'I'll tell you.' So I started over to where the skins of them sheep was. Let's see, the bear had killed seven of 'em as I rec'lect. Rufe come along with me. I picked up some of them sheep skins an' told Rufe to pick up the rest. We went back to where Mister Bear was.

"We found him, right in the same place. Hadn't wandered off at all. 'What you goin' to do?' says Rufe.

" 'I'm goin' to give this bear a new hide,' I says. An' I walked up to the bear.

" 'He'll kill you,' says Rufe. But Rufe was wrong. There warn't no more fight in that bear.

"I took a sheep skin an' shook it out a bit, makin' sure to see it was clean on the inside, didn't have no burrs or leaves or sticks or nothin' on it. This was goin' to be a pretty ticklish business an' I didn't want to make no mistake.

"I got out my knife an' trimmed the edges. Always

28

had a knife with me in them early days. No better knife ever made then the one I had. Fin'lly I got the sheep skin nice an' clean an' trimmed, an' I put it on Mister Bear an' pressed it down firm, takin' keer to be keerful, 'cause the bear was kinda tender.

"Like I say, I pressed the raw side down on the raw Mister Bear. I done the same thing with the second sheep skin. By that time Rufe had caught on to what I was doin' an' he begun to help me. Both of us workin' together, it didn't take long to git Mister Bear covered with them sheep skins. We pressed them down smooth an' neat, like we was paperin' a wall. Fin'lly we got him all covered up with sheep skins right down to his toenails.

"Wal, sir, d'you know that bear perked right up. But he was actin' funny. Not like a bear. He was waggin' his ears an' twitchin' his nose, an' swishin' his tail.

"Pretty soon he was feelin' real chipper an' he started walkin'. No, that ain't right. He sort of minced, actin' real dainty. He would hop over tree limbs that was layin' on the ground, an' bushes an' all.

"Then he give a real jump, an' made a noise, only the noise didn't sound like a growl. It sounded more like a *baa, baa*. But big. Like a fog horn down in Casco Bay. When he done that, I see he was shyin' away from another bear that was moseyin' along.

"He was the most skittish critter I ever see, almost. Then all of a sudden it comes to me that he was actin' more like a sheep than a bear. An' it was true, too. He

29

begun to nibble at the grass an' to munch on tender green leaves. Jest as soon as he got kind of comfortable in them sheep skins, he started to act like a sheep. I never thought 'bout it before then, but if you stop to consider it, it does sound reasonable.

"That bear took up with other sheep an' he grazed with 'em, an' acted jest like he was a sheep." The story-teller paused to light a match and apply it to his pipe.

"You know, I told a feller 'bout this once, an' he sort of acted like he didn't believe it. But then, there is a lot of skeptical people in the world. Untrustin' an' suspicious. I guess it's jest the nature of some folks, though I can't understand it, havin' such a trustin' nature myself."

He paused again. The match had gone out. He tapped the pipe, adjusted the tobacco, reached for another match. No one interrupted.

"Where was I? Oh, yes. 'Bout that bear. He went right on actin' like a sheep. Never seemed to be able to git it out of his head that he was a bear in sheep's clothin'. He stayed right with the flock, nibblin' grass an' hay an' all. When he'd let out that big, bass voice *baaa,* it would 'most skeer the rest of the sheep out of their wits.

"An' d'you know, I used to git two hundred pounds of wool from that critter ever' spring. I always thought that was real curious. Yup. Real curious."

The Tame Trout

"Oh, these fish are smart, all right," said one of the guests.

"They are indeed," another agreed. "There is one over at the point that I have been trying to catch for many years."

"Yes, I know. They know when you are fishing for them."

31

"Some people think fish are dumb. Just fish. But I tell you they are smart."

"Yes, they certainly are."

Uncle Ed seemed not to be listening. He sat gazing into the fire. "I once had a fish that I calc'late was 'bout the smartest fish that ever was," he said quietly.

"Tell us about it, Mr. Grant."

"Wal, sir, seein' it's you, I'll do it," the Sage of Beaver Pond said. He ran his hand over his beard thoughtfully, as if trying to generate clear memory.

"I warn't fishin' that day. Jest rowin' back from 'cross the pond. I was s'prized when this little trout made a long graceful jump out of the water an' landed right at my feet. He was a little feller, mebby not more'n six inches long.

"Wal, thinks I, that is 'bout the stupidest thing I ever see a trout do. But I was wrong. By gorry, I was wrong." The old man meditated at length.

"I leaned over an' picked the little shaver up, an' tossed him back in the pond. He didn't flap an' try to git away. I only glanced at him, but I see that he was a spritely little feller, handsome as could be. Jest as I let him go, I had a feelin' that I shouldn't of done it. That I should've kep' him. Jest why, I didn't know. Anyways, it was too late. He was gone.

"I picked up the oars agin. An' what d'you know. I'll be jiggered if that little feller didn't jump right back in the boat.

"Wal, sir, there he was agin. An' by gorry, I almost tossed him back in agin, 'spite of them thoughts I'd had. This time it must of bin the wistful look in his eyes. He was settin' there in the bottom of the boat in a little bit of water that was there. I just kep' on rowin', watchin' him an' noticin' how happy an' comfortable he seemed jest to be there.

"When I got to shore, I got me a bucket an' filled it half full of water an' took him up to the camp. Rufe Crosby was there. Him and I was trappin' together then. I got me a half of an old pork barrel we had there an' put some water in it. Rufe saw what I was doin'. 'What you got there?' he says.

"I showed him, an' he says, 'What you goin' to do with that fish?'

" 'This,' I says, 'is the most interestin' an' unusual trout in the world.'

" 'What is there so unusual about that little runt?' he asked me.

" 'This fish has intelligence. He's smart,' I told him.

"He snorted, an' I told him, 'No other fish kin hold a candle to this one.'

"I could tell it was a fish that was diff'rent. He had a high forehead. His brow swept back, sort of. He was unusual wide between the ears. But, you know, he didn't only look smart. He was handsome. Pretty, even. His fins slanted jest right. There was a dimple in his chin. He had long, arched eyebrows an' a gentle curve to his cheek that I never see in no other trout before or since.

"An' I told Rufe. 'Look at them eyes,' I says. 'They ain't only for seein'. They ain't only beautiful. They show an understandin' nature. They show character.'

"I put the little shaver in the barrel. He swum 'round a few times, an' I jest knew that trout would be remembered forever, an' cause me to be remembered, too. No other trout was ever like it, or ever will be. That trout was Ed Grant's tame trout. I kin tell you, I never see such a fish!

"I bored a little hole down right next to the bottom, an' whittled a plug an' put it in the hole. I pushed the barrel under some alders out back of the camp. It was a fine place for him. There was some overhanging goldenrod an' thistles. It was hid well, but a little sunlight splashed through.

"That trout was happy, I kin tell you. I reached down an' scratched the back of his head. He always did like that, an' he jest set there flutterin' his fins an' quiverin' his gills.

"When he got settled, I decided it was time to start trainin' him. First off, I taught him to come when I whistled for him. I always had a feelin' that a critter, whether dog or pig or fish, warn't worth his salt if he wouldn't come when he was called. When he come, I always scratched the back of his neck 'cause he liked it so much. But when I was scratchin' his neck with one hand, I was pullin' the plug with the other an' lettin' some water escape. Pretty soon, the water got lower an' lower.

"Then, ever' once in a while, I took the fish out of the tub. Jest a little while at first, then for a longer time. First, I took him out in the early mornin' when the dew was on the grass. 'Course, at first, I used swamp grass. The little feller got along fine an' didn't seem to miss water much. He splashed around in the green grass jest like he used to in green water. But he warn't color blind. I was sure of that.

"Fin'lly I put him down in the cool damp shade of the woods. He flipped an' flopped, an' I scratched the back of his neck, rewardin' him like.

"I got to takin' little walks through the woods, an' he follered me, regardless of water, dew, swamp grass, plain grass, blue grass, or sunshine.

"All this time the water was gittin' lower an' lower in his tub, count of, like I said, I was always pullin' the plug out. Fin'lly there warn't enough there for an ant to drink. Fact of the matter is, two ants fell in it one day an' died of thirst.

"Then one day I went out to see my tame trout an' there he was in the bottom of the tub gaspin'. I tell you I was some bothered. What had gone wrong? I didn't know. He had bin gittin' along fine. He had bin out of water for a long time. Why should he need it now? Why? That's what bothered me.

35 1158504

"I puzzled over that, I kin tell you. The poor little feller was in bad shape. I had to find out what was wrong quick or he'd be a goner.

"All at once it come to me. Take me for a fool, I says to myself. What have I done? I went for the camp jest as fast as I could. I got me a saucer an' put it on the bottom of the tub. Then I filled it with water. That poor little pantin' trout flapped his way to that saucer and I kin tell you he put his little face in it, an' did he drink! I should say he did. He only paused to roll his eyes up at me to show how thankful he was.

" 'Why, you poor little feller,' I says. 'I clean forgot you might want a drink. You was jest dyin' on your fins from thirst.'

"Then, I thinks, he prob'ly needs somethin' to eat, so I started to give him some flies. But that little trout didn't want nothin' give to him. He wanted to ketch 'em hisself. So I took him in the camp where he could ketch flies. I kin tell you, he kep' that camp clean of flies. Captured 'em right and left. Never seen such a hunter.

"Got so ever'where I went that trout would come along with me, flippity-flip-flappin' behind. He was the first an' only land-goin' trout in the world.

"One day I thought I'd show him off, so I put him on the ground an' started off. Rufe, he was settin' 'side of the camp door sunnin' hisself. So I started walkin' past him. He looked at me. Then he heard the sound.

That gentle, little, soft sound. Flip, flap, flippity, flip, flap, flap.

"Rufe looked at me. Then he looked around. Fi-n'lly his eyes settled on a spot 'bout four feet back of me. I kin tell you, I never see a more s'prized man in my life. His eyes was buggin' out 'bout an inch. 'Gorry! By gorry!' was all he could say.

"I set down on a log on the other side of the door. Rufe's eyes follered the little fish as he flippity-flip-flapped along in front of him. Rufe couldn't think of a thing to say as he watched that trout flap an' flip around in a tiny circle an' fin'lly rest his chin on my shoe.

"I taught that tame trout to set up, an' how to speak, an' shake fins, to roll over, an' to flip through a hoop. 'Course he could hunt, too. Was a great one for ketchin' flies an' such. I was figgerin' to make a mouser out of him when he got bigger, an' when he really got his growth, I was goin' to teach him how to hunt rab-bits. Coons even, mebby.

"As it was, he was doin' fine. He 'most kep' the camp clean of flies an' mosquiters. An' growin'. My, how he growed! 'Course he had some trouble, like gittin' his gills caught in the tall grass sometimes. But I'd help him git untangled an' off he'd go agin, flippin' an' flappin'.

"Then there come a day." The old man paused. His voice throbbed a bit, and he seemed to try to swallow

37

a deep emotion that surged up within him.

"Yes, sir," he continued bravely. "There come a day. Rufe was settin' on the bench near the door. I had to go down to the pond to look at some traps I had set there. I starts off, an' that trout come a-flippity-flip-flappin' after me.

"The path run 'cross a brook, an' over this brook there was kind of a bridge made of three spruce logs layin' together. I went right 'cross it. The trout was comin' after me, flippin' and flappin' his way as hard as he could.

"I looked back. There he was a-comin'. He was on the center log, goin' at a great rate. All at once I knowed somethin' was wrong. But it was too late. His left hind fin caught on a piece of bark. He half turned, an' lost his balance, an' fell.

"There was a crack between the logs an' the poor little rascal dropped right through it an' fell into the water with a plop. There was a deep pool right there. I stood on the bank watchin' the circles spread out across the water.

"That was all there was. Ever'thing was quiet. Seemed to me like even the locusts stopped their chirpin' for a minute. The wind died down. It was quiet. Not even the lily pads stirred.

"I tried to do somethin'. I went an' reached down ready to scoop him out if I could see him. But, no. It was no use. He was gone. He had lived out of water

38

for so long he had forgot how to swim. He drowned."

The old man raised his gnarled hand and seemed to knuckle away a tear. There was another long, emotion-filled pause. The only noise in the room was the punctuation marks supplied by the crackling fire.

"I kin tell you," he continued, "thoughts was rushin' through my head like swarmin' bees. But now I think 'bout it, mebby it was jest as well. It might be that he never would have learned to hunt for game. He might of turned out to be jest an ordinary house fish, an' no hunter at all. Yup. Prob'ly it was jest as well that way. I'm sure he couldn't have learned to travel in the snow, an' I declare, I wouldn't have knowed how to make a pair of snowshoes for him."

Mount Kennebago

Beaver Pond is at the source of the Kennebago River, not far north of the tree-studded valley where it dances its way between Kennebago Mountain and Cow Ridge, where it skips between the White Cap and the Boil Mountains. Beaver Pond shares the honor of giving birth to the Kennebago with several other ponds. They call it the Seven Ponds District, but the map says there are more than seven: Long Pond, Secret Pond, L Pond, Little Island Pond, Big Island Pond, Northwest Pond, Little Northwest Pond, South Boundary Pond, and Rock Pond.

All of these clearly find their names in some characteristic they possess. But one more pond remains. With justice, it is named after a man. It is Grant Pond.

All of this geography is within half-a-dozen miles of the Canadian border and the same distance southwest of Chain of Ponds. It is thirty miles in the deep woods north of the town of Rangeley and Rangeley Lake and the beautiful lake known as Mooselookmeguntic—which should be pronounced carefully and slowly to get the full flavor and whose strange name had a story that Ed Grant would tell when he was in the mood.

One day two young men approached Uncle Ed's camp at Beaver Pond. He was seated in the shade near the door and he seemed to be asleep. The men had never been to the camps before and they did not know Uncle Ed. His beard bristled with gray. His plaid wool shirt collar was open at the neck and his battered felt hat was shading his closed eyes.

The young men should have respected the repose of an old man who appeared to be asleep, but they did not. One of them nudged Uncle Ed. He moved restlessly and mumbled something in a low voice.

The young man nudged him again and said, "Nice day."

"Yup," came a sleepy voice through the graying beard. Uncle Ed slowly opened an eye. Its bright blue gaze settled on the young man.

"What do you do around here, old fellow?" the young man asked.

"Oh, jest stay hereabouts."

"You live here?"

"Yup." The other eye opened.

"How long have you lived here, old fellow?"

After a long pause the eyes dropped and Uncle Ed looked off toward Kennebago Mountain in the distance.

"See that mountain over there?" he asked.

The men followed his gaze. "Yes," they replied.

"Wal," Ed Grant said, "When I first come here, that mountain was jest a little hill."

"Uh — " There seemed no suitable comment.

"Yup. An' it was 'bout four miles from where it is now. Over to the left there."

Instinctively the young men turned their heads to the left. Uncle Ed continued.

"The first thing I done when I come up here from Rangeley was to build me this camp to live in. Wal, sir, after I got it built, it dawned on me that that there little hill was spoilin' my view, what with it facin' the way it did an' all. You kin jest imagine how mad that made me, destroyin' my view of the country. So one day, I jest made up my mind I couldn't stand for it no more. I hitched up my team. They was the best woods hosses 'round here. Tom an' Jerry, they was named. Yup. They was sure a good team of hosses. Stood about seventeen hands high. Come close to weighin' a ton each, when they was fat.

"Wal, sir, I went over to that little hill an' I hitched ol' Tom an' Jerry up to it. It was a stubborn hill, I kin tell you. Fastened down real firm, it was. Must of been because of the tree roots lacin' through all the rocks. Yup. That hill was fastened down real firm. I had to pull on it for the best part of two weeks. But fin'lly she begun to give. Slow at first. But she kep' comin' 'cause I kep' ol' Tom an' Jerry pullin' at it. After a time I got it pulled to where I wanted it. Like I say, that's 'bout four miles, to the spot where she is today. I had some trouble gittin' her placed jest right, but fin'lly she was restin' nice an' easy.

"An' d'you know, it turned out the soil was pretty good there. Better'n I thought, to tell you the truth. That little hill took root right away, an' soon it growed an' growed until it become a mountain. We call it Kennebago Mountain. That's because the Kennebago Indians used to live hereabouts."

Uncle Ed slowly closed his eyes again, and the two young men silently turned away.

The Tale of a Watch

"What is the best bait for trout, Mr. Grant?"

It was an old question. An ever-present question among the visitors at Beaver Pond.

"Jest depends," replied Uncle Ed. "Depends on what the trout is eatin' that day, or that minute, for that matter. A trout will take most anything, but he'll take it in his own time. The trick is to know jest what an' when. I seen trout take some mighty curious things in my day."

"What was the most curious thing?"

"Wal, seein' it's you, I'll tell you. We was havin' pretty good fishin' then. It happened over on Mooselookmeguntic Lake."

"That's a strange name. I suppose it's an Indian name?"

"Wal, sort of. At least, that's what they say." The old man pulled out his pipe and fondled it lovingly.

"Do you know how it got its name?"

"Yup. Least I know what they say. I wouldn't vouch for the truth of it. Warn't there at the time, so I don't like to say it's the precise exact truth. Feller can't be too keerful 'bout makin' sure he always tells the truth. If you don't know it's true, be sure to say so. That's what I always say.

"The story they tell is that in the early days an Indian went out on the lake huntin'. He was in a canoe. A moose came down to the edge of the lake. The Indian lifted his gun. 'Course it was one of them old-fashioned muzzle loaders with a flint an' pan for firin', an' sometimes they didn't go off. Warn't no spark, or the powder was wet, or it warn't fixed jest right, or somethin'.

"This Indian ketched sight of the moose. He lifted his gun. The moose lifted his head up an' looked straight at the Indian. Then the Indian aims, an' pulls the trigger. But the gun didn't go off. When the hammer hit, it jest went *tick*. Like that. *Tick,* instead of goin' *bang,* y'see.

"The moose turns and runs away an' the Indian come back to camp. They asked him what had happened out on the lake. 'Course he didn't speak English very good, so when he told them what happened, he said 'Moose look. Me gun tick.' So after that, they called the lake Mooselookmeguntic.

"Now don't go 'round tellin' folks that's what happened, an' that Ed Grant says so. Mebby it did, an' mebby it didn't. I warn't there, so I can't say for sure. I got a reputation for tellin' the truth. I always like to make sure I don't tell no more than the precise exact truth."

The old man loaded his pipe with meticulous deliberation and care. "Let's see," he said. "We was talkin' 'bout somethin' else. Where was I?"

"You were talking about some curious trout bait," said a helpful listener.

"Nope, 'twarn't that. Nope. 'Twarn't bait. It was jest a curious thing that happened 'bout what a trout et. It was a watch."

"A watch?"

"A trout ate a watch?"

"Yup. A solid gold watch. A repeater. Struck on the quarter hour, half-hour, an' hour, y'know. I was guidin' this sport. Martin, his name was. Feller from

New York. Nice feller. Real sportsman, he was. Wal, he was gittin' some real good fishin'. Havin' a great day. Then he looks at his watch. It was valuable. I could tell that jest by lookin' at it. Real gold. All of a sudden, it slips out of his hand, an' jest at that precise self-same minute the snap on the watch chain broke.

"It fell, *kerplunk.* An' no sooner had it hit the water than a trout struck it. Big feller, he was. Wal, you kin tell he must of bin big, for he opens his mouth an' takes that watch an' swallers it, an' down an' away he goes. So it stands to reason he was big.

" 'Course this Mr. Martin, he was powerful amazed. An' he was mad, too, losin' his watch like that, not only 'cause it was a valuable solid gold watch, but it was give to him by his paw.

"Next year I was guidin' the same feller agin. We was out on Lake Mooselookmeguntic, not far from where he was the year before. All of a sudden he gits a strike. It was a big fish an' he had his hands full for a time, I kin tell you. That fish put up quite a fight an' almost got away more'n a couple of times.

"But fin'lly he was captured. That fish was jest 'bout as big as trout come. I have seen bigger, but not much, an' this feller, he says he's going to have him mounted.

"The fish was there in the bottom of the boat, an'

48

all of a sudden we hear a noise. Like a bell, it was. *Ding, ding, ding.*

" 'What's that?' he says.

" 'Must of bin a dinner bell somewheres,' says I.

"In 'bout fifteen minutes, we hear another sound. *Ding, ding, ding.* Jest like that.

" 'There's that bell again,' he says.

"It was curious. Least that's the way it struck me, 'cause I didn't know of no bells 'round like that. Then 'bout fifteen minutes later, there it goes agin. *Ding, ding, ding.*

"By now I was beginnin' to smell a rat. I had bin doin' some figgerin' an' when we heerd it agin, I gets an idee. I picked up that fish an' put it up to my ear, an' I hear *tick, tick, tick, tick.*

"I opened the fish, an' would you believe it? There, inside that fish, was that feller's watch. Tickin' away an' strikin' ever' fifteen minutes, jest like when it was brand new. It had only gained two minutes in the whole year it was lost, too.

"I was puzzled some over that, an' I figgered that the watch was kep' wound up by the fish always wigglin' this way an' that way as he swum along. I kin usually figger an answer for curious things like that if I puzzle over 'em long enough."

A Long Shot

"I rec'lect the longest shot I ever made," said Uncle Ed. "For that matter, I guess it must of bin 'bout the longest shot anybody ever made."

"Tell us about it, Mr. Grant," someone said. It was not really necessary to ask. Ed Grant had an audience. They were eager to listen. A story would unfold.

"Wal, sir, I was a young feller then an' did a good

deal of huntin'. I had a big gun. An old one, but as straight a shooter as I ever see. I can't jest tell you how big the ball was. She was a muzzle loader. But that ball was considerable bigger than a baseball. 'Course it took plenty of powder to fire it. I used to put salt in, too. On top of the powder, an' underneath the ball."

"What was that for?"

"Yes. Why did you put the salt in?"

"Wal, you see I'd oftentimes git a real long shot with that gun. So I put the salt in to keep the game from spoilin' while it was droppin' to the ground. Some of 'em had to drop a considerable distance sometimes. That was an idee of my own. An invention I invented. Then, too, 'course the bird is already seasoned, an' you don't have to salt it when you cook it.

"You kin best tell 'bout that gun when I tell you 'bout that long shot I made. Wal, sir, there was this partridge. He was a big one, and nobody could shoot him. So I set out to do it. Seems like he'd gone crazy, an' was goin' 'round destroyin' other partridge nests.

"So I loaded up my old gun, an' off I goes. He was over there on the other side of Boil Mountain. 'Course it warn't long before I got him in my sights. I drawed a bead on him, an' I kin tell you he was a-flyin' for all he was worth.

"He was whirrin' along, beatin' his wings fast as a hummin' bird. Like I say, I got him in my sights. He was a-flyin' straight away from me, so I figgers it's an easy shot. I fires. *Bang!* An' Mister Partridge puts on more speed still, an' out of sight he goes behind a clump of birches on top of a hill.

"So I walked on, expectin' to pick him up. But, do you know, I couldn't find that critter anywheres. Looked ever'wheres. Yup. I'd missed him, I figgered, so I went back to camp. Couldn't understand it. I had him right in my sights. I had took ever'thing into consideration, like the wind, the powder, an' like that. But there warn't no answer. I'd jest missed him. That was all. First time I ever missed a shot, too. I kin tell you I didn't say nothin' to nobody 'bout it. I'd of sooner took a whippin'.

"Wal, sir. It was 'bout three weeks later. My brother John come up here. He was workin' then on a schooner in the coast trade, runnin' from Halifax to Boston.

"We was talkin', John an' me, an' he says, 'Did you take a shot at a partridge Thursday two week ago?'

" 'Why, yes,' I says. I didn't figger there was any use denyin' it. Anyways, I didn't see how he could guess any such thing. 'How did you know?' I asked him.

" 'Wal,' he says, 'we was coastin' along, 'bout ten mile off the shore that day, an' I heerd a noise like a partridge flyin'. It puzzled me some. I was up on the top mast at the time, takin' in some sail. All of a sudden I see this partridge comin'. He whizzed right past me.

" 'He was a-goin' some, I kin tell you,' John says.

53

'I don't think I ever see a sorrier partridge. He was shy some feathers, an' the sweat was rollin' off his beak. All in all, I don't think I ever see a harder-workin' or faster-flyin' partridge,' he says.

" 'Then,' John says, 'the next thing I see was even stranger than that.'

" 'What was that?' I asked him.

" 'Why,' he says, 'right after that bird, 'bout twenty, twenty-two inches, come a bullet, an' I knowed it was your bullet,' he says.

" 'How did you know it was mine?' I asked him.

" 'Wal,' he says. 'Anyone knows what a bullet from that old gun of yours looks like. No one else shoots a bullet that big, an' it had that special mark you put on your bullets. An' that bullet was tearin' along right behind Mister Partridge. It was headed straight for him, tryin' its best to ketch up with the bird. It was a-rarin' and a-tearin', goin' straight as a die, but it was a little wore down at the edges from buckin' the wind. It was a race I won't soon forgit,' he says. 'What had happened?'

"So I told him. Told him how I had shot at the partridge, and couldn't find him.

"An' John says, 'I sure would like to know what happened after that. The last time I see that bird an' bullet, they was both tearin' past me right out to sea, an' I never see 'em agin.' "

"My, that was strange," said one of the guests.

"But that ain't all," the Sage of Beaver Pond continued. "Seven years later, in midsummer it was, I was standin' down by the pond when I heerd sort of a whirrin' sound. Then, directly, a sort of a dull thud. Right at my feet, it was. I looked down. There was a little cloud of dust there. Then another tiny plop an' I see sort of a little white cloud come up an' settle down. It all happened quick. An' do you know what? There at my feet was a partridge. No, that ain't right. It was what used to be a partridge. 'Twarn't much more than a skeleton. His hide was 'most all wore off. He didn't have no breast nor back feathers at all. His comb an' wattles was all wore down to nothin', an' his wings was practic'lly wore down to stubs. He only had two tail feathers left, an' they was knotted an' lumpy, like the rag tail of a kite. No meat on him at all.

"An' back of that bird, 'bout eighteen, twenty inches, was a little round thing. I picks it up an' looks at it. An' do you know, it was my bullet, with this little white cloud settlin' round it. The same one I had shot at the partridge seven years before. I could tell it was mine 'count of a special mark I put on all my bullets. But it warn't like a baseball no more. It warn't no bigger than a buckshot. Must of bin wore down by the friction an' the wind an' like that.

"Then 'course I figgered it out and knowed what had happened. That partridge had flew 'round the earth. I calc'lated it later, an' the way I figgered it, he had flew 'round the earth twelve thousand, six hundred an' seventy-two times. That partridge was goin' fast, an' the air pressure in front of the bullet pushed him along. An' the vacuum behind the bird sort of pulled the bullet along. I figgered that was prob'ly the longest shot anybody ever made."

"What was that little white cloud you mentioned, Mr. Grant?" asked one of the guests.

"Oh, that? Wal, I always figgered that was the salt. Don't know whether it done anything 'bout keepin' the bird from spoilin' though."

Uncle Ed Is Chased by a Bear

"Seems like all my life I been havin' to do with bears," said Uncle Ed.

Dinner was over and the group around the fire paused expectantly. Uncle Ed Grant was going to tell a story. Now the beautiful day in the Maine woods would be complete. The folks in the room waited as Uncle Ed paused, while his mind went back over the events that were about to come to life.

"I don't much like to talk 'bout bears, 'cause it seems like I bin runnin' away from a good many of 'em. A body might think I ain't as brave as I might be."

"What did you run for?" asked one of the young sportsmen.

" 'Cause I didn't want him to ketch me," Uncle Ed replied. "Never did much want to be a bear's breakfast."

"Why didn't you shoot him?"

Uncle Ed turned and looked at his questioner. "Didn't have a gun," he said. "It was rough up here then. I should of had a gun. But I didn't."

"And you met a bear out in the woods?"

"Yup. Met him face to face one day when I was pickin' blueberries. That's the reason I didn't have a gun. You don't need a gun to pick blueberries. Ever'body knows that. 'Cept the bear. He didn't know it. So there he was."

"Gee!"

"Yup. There he was, and there I was. I begun doin' some tall thinkin', I kin tell you. He was a mighty big bear. He had a forehead that looked like a twenty dollar roll-top desk."

"What did you do?"

"Do? I already told you. I turned an' run. That's what I did."

"What did the bear do?"

"I already told you that, too. He run after me. I

never see such a determined bear — or such a fast one, for that matter. Fin'lly Mister Bear was gittin' too close for comfort. He was gainin' on me. No wonder, him havin' four legs, and me havin' only two. It stands to reason I would have trouble keepin' out of his reach, even though I was considered a real fast runner in them days. You kin understand that, of course?"

Uncle Ed directed his question to the young sportsman who had been questioning him, a young man named Ralph Howard who was at the camps for the first time. Ralph was eagerly taking in every word that came from the lips of the Sage of Beaver Pond. "Yes," he said "Certainly."

"Like I say," Ed Grant continued, "I was runnin' as hard as I could. I ain't goin' to take time to tell you ever' single thing that happened. Like as not, I couldn't remember ever' single thing now anyways. That happened a long time ago.

"But I rec'lect what I felt like when I saw a branch on a tree stickin' out. 'Course I was in the woods. Deep woods, an' all the branches was 'way up high. This one was up kind of high, too, but, thinks I, if I kin jest jump up high enough to reach that limb, I kin git away from Mister Bear's reach."

Uncle Ed paused. He bent down and picked up the poker. The firelight shone on his honest, rough face. It was clear that he was painfully reaching through his memory for a clearer picture of his race with the bear.

He poked the fire. His lips pursed as he seemed to search for the words that would properly relate his experience.

He gave the burning embers a last skillful touch with the poker and sat down. "Yup. I was quite a jumper in my day," he went on. His audience was silent. Intent.

"So I got ready as I run, an' jest at the precise proper time I jumped! That was quite a jump, I kin tell you. It was a good jump, all right. It was too good. That's what was the matter with it. I jumped too high, an' I went right past that branch I was aimin' for."

"No!" said Ralph.

"Yup. Right past it. Up I went, right past that limb."

"Were you hurt?"

"Nope."

"Well, what happened?"

"Wal, thinks I, this is bad."

"I should think so."

"But of course I started to fall right back down when I reached the top of my jump. An', by gorry, do you know what?"

"No. What?" asked Ralph.

"I caught that branch on the way down! Lucky, warn't I?"

"You certainly were," Ralph agreed enthusiastically.

"But not for long. I didn't quite git settled on that branch when *crack!* it broke. An' down to the ground

I come." He leaned forward in his chair and put the poker on the hearth.

"But no harm was done," he went on, " 'cause Mister Bear was havin' some trouble of his own. When I jumped he didn't know for sure what had happened an' anyway, he was goin' so fast he couldn't stop. So he skidded on for a while before he could slide to a halt. By the time he had got hisself stopped, turned around, an' squared around an' all, I had done all my over-jumpin', fallin', limb-breakin', an' still more fallin', an' I was high-tailin' it in the opposite direction.

"Wal, sir, that bear was after me agin. Lickety-split I went, an' pell-mell he come after me. Like I say, I don't jest rec'lect ever'thing that happened. Not ever' little detail, that is. An' I wouldn't have time to tell you if I did, 'cause it's gittin' late an' we ought to go to bed pretty soon. But I s'pose you want to know what fin'lly happened?"

"Yes," Ralph breathed. "What happened?"

"Like I say, I was a-runnin', an' the bear was a-runnin'. I come to a pond. I run across all right, an' the bear follered me, but the ice was too thin to hold him, him bein' so much heavier. So when he got in the middle of the pond, the ice went *crack, crackety, crack* an' it broke. Mister Bear jest natur'lly fell through, an' he was drowned."

Uncle Ed was silent. The guests were silent. The silence was thundering. Finally Ralph spoke. "Well —

61

Why, Mr. Grant — I remember — I think you said you were out picking blueberries."

"Yup. That's right."

"Well, then. Where did the ice come from? If you were picking blueberries, there wouldn't be any ice, would there?"

"I told you I couldn't tell you ever'thing that happened," said the Sage of Beaver Pond. "An' I guess I must of neglected to tell you that that bear chased me from August to November."

Uncle Ed rose. He yawned and said, "Wal, it's gittin' past my bed time. Good night."

The New Camp Stove

It was another one of those evenings. Just the kind for one of Uncle Ed Grant's yarns. The fire was burning brightly. The soft, wavering light of the flames created little shadows that danced lightly in the half-darkness, out of time with the small crackling and bold popping of the burning wood. The guests were silent, each intent on his own thoughts as he faced the flames.

"The fire feels good, doesn't it?" said one.

"Yes. Don't you love the smell of the burning wood?" said another.

"Did you build the fireplace yourself, Mr. Grant?"

"Yup. Always build the fireplaces m'self. Can't trust that to nobody else," replied Uncle Ed. "I always was able to get a good draft. There's quite a trick to it. You got to know jest how to do it. Speakin' of drafts, that puts me in mind of a camp stove I had once. Jeehosiphat! but that stove had a draft!"

"Tell us about it, Mr. Grant."

"Wal, seein' it's you, I'll do it." The Sage of Beaver Pond reached for his pipe and settled down to the business of lighting it, the usual accompaniment to a good tale. "It was in the early days. This stove was an invention of mine. I had the blacksmith out to Rangeley make it for me. I give him the measurements an' the design. It had to be packed up here. Hard thing to pack, it was. Kep' slippin'. Hard to get it loaded on a body's back. But that's somethin' else.

" 'Course I got her up here, an' I got her installed. I didn't know it then, but it was a good thing, 'cause that was the year we didn't have no summer. We had a snow. I thought it was jest a late snow. It was cold, an' I was glad I got her installed.

"Rufe Crosby an' Elmer Snowman was here. They was guidin' then. So was John Meader. An' with them was a man named — let's see. Oh, yes. Jackson. Mr.

Jackson. He was from Bangor. Then there was another Bangor man, name of Mr. Grilling. Then, let's see. There was a man name of Mr. Stephens, too. He was from Portland. This Mr. Jackson was a short feller. Fat. An' he had a wart on his nose.

" 'Course they was all interested in the new stove. This Mr. Jackson claimed he knowed somethin' 'bout stoves. He didn't say much, but I knowed he thought it never would draw. He was a nice feller, though. I never did hold that agin him.

"So when they come in that night I had Missus Stove all ready. 'Now,' I says to them. 'It's good an' cold to-night, so we kin have a fair trial an' see 'bout Missus Stove's draft, an' all.'

" 'Let's start her up,' says Rufe. 'It's colder than the tips of a snowbird's wings.'

" 'I guess she's ready,' says John. John Meader, that was. John, he thought the stove was goin' to be jim dandy. But then John knowed that when I put m'self to it, I was pretty good at inventin' things.

"I turned to Mr. Jackson. 'You start her, Mr. Jackson,' I says to him. I jest wanted to see his expression when that stove started, him not thinkin' it would work, y'know?

" 'All right,' he says. He was kinda amused, but he was pleased enough that he had the honor of startin' my new stove. He put in some dry wood an' struck a match.

" 'Looks like it might be all right,' he says, kinda like he didn't know whether to believe it or not.

" 'Boys,' says I, 'shuck your coats, 'cause when this stove gits operatin', you won't need 'em.'

"Ever'body was interested an' was watchin'. 'Guess you got her installed right,' says Mr. Jackson.

" 'Course, he didn't seem to realize that there ain't much to installin' a stove. It's inventin' 'em that's the trick.

"Mr. Jackson, he was puttin' on more wood, an' I told him to be keerful. You can't be too cautious 'bout things like that. I knowed that stove would draw, but I was more'n a mite dubious 'bout the way he was puttin' on wood.

" 'Don't worry,' says this Mr. Jackson. 'I know 'bout stoves. I got three of 'em back in my house up to Bangor,' he says.

" 'But take it easy,' I kep' sayin'. 'That stove is specially invented to have a strong draft.'

"We shucked our coats an' ever' time Mr. Jackson took off the lid that fire'd shine on his face, an' the wart on his nose would throw a shadow 'cross his cheek.

" 'She's goin' to be goin' too strong,' I says, 'if you ain't keerful.'

" 'No, she needs more wood,' he says. 'It's a cold night.'

" 'Course he was right. It was a cold night. But the sportsman has to rely on the guide in the woods, an'

here he was handlin' a stove. He thought he knowed
'bout stoves, so he wanted to show ever'body how much
he knowed. So he kep' on a-stuffin' wood into that
stove. The way he done it was a caution, I kin tell you.

"The sides of the stove started to get pink, like a
blushin' schoolgirl. Then it spread an' got a deeper
red, an' deeper, until it started to look like the top
of a red-headed woodpecker. The wood was a-poppin'
an' a-snappin' like a Fourth o' July celebration.

" 'That stove is a-gittin' too hot too fast,' I says.

" 'You're right,' says Rufe, movin' back his chair
an' unbuttonin' his collar. Ever'body done the same
thing 'cause now that stove was startin' to turn white.
The poppin' an' snappin' turned into a roar as the
air got sucked into the damper.

" 'We got to do somethin' 'bout that stove,' says I.

" 'That's right. But what?' says Rufe.

"Before I could answer, there was a sound. *Zup!*
Jest like that. Then there was a rattle.

"I looks at the stove. 'Look at that!' I hollers. Ever'-
body looked jest in time to see the poker fly from the
floor to the open damper at the bottom of the stove.

" 'It's the draft,' I yells. 'That draft is so strong it
sucked the poker right into the fire.'

"*Zup!* The lid lifter which had bin layin' on the
floor was sucked into the damper by the draft. It rattled from side to side in the damper before it was
sucked up.

"*Zup!* In flew the shovel, an' it rattled its death rattle against the sides before it disappeared.

" 'I never knowed a draft could be so strong,' I says to m'self.

" 'Look!' yells John.

"But there warn't no need to yell. Ever'body saw it. Right before our eyes that new camp stove rose right up from off the floor. Good thing it did, too, for the legs was gittin' hot an' the floor was beginnin' to burn where they touched.

"We stood there, for all of us had kicked our chairs away by this time, an' we see that stove rise up, being sucked up by the strongest draft any stove ever had.

" 'We got to do somethin', says I.

" 'Jeehosiphat! You're right,' says Rufe.

" 'If we don't, no tellin' what might happen,' says I. An' that was right, too. That draft was on its way to suckin the stove right through the roof. If that happened, the stove might get lost, for with all that pressure, she would go sailin' off in the sky to no tellin' where.

" 'What kin we do?' Elmer yelled.

" 'We got to stay calm,' I says. 'We got to cool Missus Stove off, that's what we got to do.'

"It all happened quick. Not more'n five, six minutes. Mebby seven. Good, dry Maine wood makes a fire quick when you got a good draft.

"That stove was rattlin' an' roarin' as the draft

68

rushed through the damper. The wood was poppin' an' snappin' an' cracklin'. The stove rose higher. It was startin' to bump agin the splits of the roof.

" 'We got to cool her off.'

" 'The stove is bangin' agin the splits!'

"Ever'body started talkin' at once. Mebby it would take the whole roof off. She was a-roarin' like a cyclone.

"Nobody was doin' anything. So it was up to me. 'Get some snow,' I says.

"They all got buckets an' come in with pails filled with snow.

" 'Push the table over here,' I says.

"Then I got up on the table. I took one of the buckets an' shoved it up under one of the stove legs. *Zip* it went, an' then it sizzled as that hot stove leg hit the snow. But it cooled off some an' the stove slipped down on that corner. Then I took another bucket of snow an' pushed it up under another leg. *Zip* and sizzle agin, an' that side dropped down a little.

" 'More snow,' says I, an' I took another bucket of snow an' with more *zip* and sizzle cooled off one of the hind legs. Down she come a little in the back corner.

"By this time the boys see what I was doin' so they takes their buckets of fresh snow an' pushes 'em up under the diff'rent legs. Jest a little bit at a time so's not to upset her or bring her down too fast. As quick as the snow melted, we got fresh snow an' kep' on a-workin'.

69

" 'Take her easy,' I kep' sayin', 'so's to keep her all comin' down steady an' even.'

"*Zip* and sizzle. *Zip* and sizzle. Down she come, slow but sure as the legs got cool an' the coolness spread up to the rest of the stove. Gentle an' easy we done it, an' down she come, until fin'lly she was restin' on the floor agin.

"Wal, sir, when we got Missus Stove down, we stepped outside to kinda cool off, it bein' such hot work. An' d'you know what?"

"No. What?" asked one of the guests.

"In spite of ever'thing, that stove had pushed up that roof so hard that it had pushed the whole camp up off of the ground an' moved it 'bout ten yards up the hill. 'Course we hadn't noticed nothin' at the time 'cause we was so busy. It must of been higher than four feet off the ground at one time 'cause it was on the other side of a woodpile that was that high. An' it stands to reason it had to be that high as long as it went over the woodpile.

"Yup. I always thought that was a curious thing. Real curious."

Minute Pudding

"It must be pretty cold up here in the winter time," one of the ladies said as she edged closer to the fire.

"Yup. It does git pretty cold," said Uncle Ed.

"And when you were trapping, did you stay out in the cold?"

" 'Course. But we got along all right."

"Didn't you have a lot of adventures?"

"Yup. But it was all in a day's work. I rec'lect one blizzard we had. I was trappin' with John Meader and Rufe Crosby. It was long towards the end of the season. The streams was free from ice an' we was jest 'bout ready to clear out and head back to Rangeley. It was right here at Beaver Pond, as a matter of fact.

"Then this blizzard come. Why, the snow was most all gone, 'cept in some places where the sun didn't git to. The pussy willows was comin' out, an' things in general was startin' to turn. Jest a slight touch of green, y'know, like when the buds first start to pop. It seemed like spring. Yup. It looked jest like spring was comin'. But this blizzard come instead. When a Maine blizzard sets in, it sets in whether spring is comin' or not.

"Wal, sir, y'know, in them days we was batchin' it, of course, so we had to do our own cookin'. The way we decided who was goin' to do the cookin' was like this. The first man who got back to camp would cook the meal.

"Nobody liked to cook much, so that way each man would stay out lookin' after his traps as long as he could, 'count of if he got in first, he would be the cook.

"The day that blizzard come, we was all in camp. Natur'lly we had to find a new way of selectin' the cook. The way we done it was to draw straws, with the understandin' that the first feller to complain 'bout the cookin' would have to be the cook till somebody else complained, an' then that complainer would have to do the cookin'."

"Well, then," interrupted one of the guests. "All the cook had to do was to cook poorly so someone would complain."

"Yup. That's right. But the cook was also eatin' the grub he cooked. If he cooked it too bad, he'd prob'ly do the complainin' hisself. So, as a result, the cookin' was pretty good. Still an' all, ever'body makes mistakes now an' then. Most ever'body, that is. An' anyways, with nothin' to do 'cept set 'round the camp, when we was all talked out anyways, somebody is bound to complain 'bout the cookin' pretty quick.

"Wal, sir, we drawed straws, an' John he got the shortest stick. He done the job all right. John was a pretty good cook. Like I say, we'd bin together, jest the three of us, all winter an' we was pretty well talked out. We had talked 'bout most ever'thing, so we talked 'bout most ever'thing agin, 'cept for one thing. We didn't talk 'bout the grub, 'count of no tellin' what might be considered a complaint.

"Three — no, four — yup, it was four days went by an' John was still doin' the cookin'. Nobody had complained 'bout the grub.

"Jest to show you how fellers like that run out of subjects to talk 'bout, we was talkin' 'bout who is the boss of a house, the woman or the man.

73

"Rufe first raised the question, an' it was a good one to talk 'bout in a blizzard. Nobody knowed the answer an' there was plenty of room for argument. Rufe figgered the woman was the boss gener'lly. John he didn't agree at all. Accordin' to him, the man wore the pants an' he was the boss. I didn't know for sure. I figgered it prob'ly was the woman who usually run things. 'Course we was all young fellers. None of us was married.

"John fin'lly admitted that a woman was likely to have a mind of her own but, like I say, he held the man was the boss.

"John said he bet the man makes the important decisions an' the woman makes the unimportant ones.

"Rufe said that was right. The wife lets the husband decide 'bout the weather, the army, an' the navy. Whether they are big enough. An' who should run for president, an' such things. An' that the wife would decide ever'thing else. Like goin' to church and socials. When to take a bath an' to shave. What to have to eat. When to go visitin' the neighbors. When to have company, an' who the company would be. When to shovel the snow an' clean the cellar. When to build a new barn. When to go to bed an' when to get up in the mornin'. Them things an' ever'thing else would be the unimportant things that the wife would decide.

" 'Course it was clear to me that under them conditions the wife would be decidin' ever'thing 'round the house, and I figgers that some day I might jest look into that question to find out for sure. Yup. Made up my mind to do it, as a matter of fact.

"But to get back to my story 'bout the cookin'. Like I say, John was a good cook, an' there warn't nothin' much to complain 'bout. Then this night he made some minute puddin'. That's made out of flour an' sugar an' water, y'know. It only takes a minute to fix it. That's why they call it minute puddin'.

"Wal, sir, we set up to the table to see what damage we could do to the vittles. The minute puddin' John made was real good as a usual thing, but that night he had forgot to mix in the flour jest right. It was lumpy. By gorry, how lumpy that puddin' was!

"When he put it on the table Rufe perked up. 'Ah,' says Rufe. 'Minute puddin'. One of my favorite dishes.'

" 'Mine, too,' says I, knowin' how good John made it. An' my mouth started a-waterin'. With that, I put a spoonful of the stuff in my mouth, an' by gorry, I bit into a lump of dry flour. 'Why,' says I to John, 'this flour ain't mixed into this minute puddin'. It's full of lumps of dry flour!'

"Jest then I ketched m'self. The first feller to complain had to take over as cook, an' I kin tell you that any look of complaint was washed right off of my face. I went right on to say real quick, 'It's jest the way I like it.'

"Wal, either I was complainin' or I warn't. An' I

warn't goin' to take no chances. So I puts a dried-up kind of smile on my face an' takes spoonful after spoonful of the stuff, lumps of dry flour an' all. I didn't know how much longer we was goin' to be snowed in, an' I warn't goin' to be the cook if I could help it.

"John an' Rufe hadn't touched their puddin' yet, an' they both stopped to watch me. I had to go ahead eatin' the stuff jest like it was good.

"John was a-puzzlin', wonderin' if I had made a complaint 'bout the grub. He says to me, 'Ed,' he says, 'was you complainin' 'bout the grub?'

" 'Who? Me?' I says, jest as innocent as I could with a mouth full of dry flour. 'Me complainin'? Why, this minute puddin' is cooked jest the way I like it.'

"Then Rufe picks up his spoon an' starts to take a big mouthful. His spoon had cut through one of them big lumps of flour. 'What's this?' he says, as he looks at the flour in his plate an' before he got the taste of flour in his mouth.

" 'Them things is the minutes in the minute puddin',' I says right quick like, an' went right on eatin'.

"Wal, I could see that Rufe didn't like that kind of minute puddin' no better than I did, but he warn't goin' to be the one to complain 'bout the grub either. That blizzard was still goin' good and no tellin' how long we'd be cooped up. Rufe done jest like I done. He set there an' ate the awful stuff an' cleaned his plate.

76

"John was the only one who didn't have to eat it, an' I kin tell you he got some pleasure out of seein' us suffer. We spent the next two days arguin' 'bout whether anybody had bin complainin' or not. Fin'lly the storm come to an end, an' John, he was still the cook."

Who Is Boss?

"Mr. Grant, did you ever find out who is the boss, the husband or the wife? You remember the question you talked about when the blizzard came?" The questioner was searching for a story. He was not to be disappointed.

"Oh, that. Wal, yup, I did," Uncle Ed replied.

"How did you go about finding out? What did you discover?" asked the guest.

THE WORLD'S MOST TRUTHFUL MAN

The Sage of Beaver Pond regarded his pipe thoughtfully. "It was real interestin'," he commented. "Like I told you, I made up my mind that I'd find out which was the boss, the husband or the wife. So that same summer — no, it was in the fall. Early in the fall. I had the time then an' that was a real puzzlin' question. But I made up my mind how I'd go 'bout it, too."

Uncle Ed tamped down the tobacco in his pipe, adjusted it first this way, then that way, seemed satisfied, and finally reached for a match. No one interrupted. The guests gathered in the big room next to the dining room were eager to hear another of Ed Grant's tales, especially one concerning so vital a question.

"I hitched up ol' Tom an' Jerry. Mebby I told you 'bout them. They was a pair of hosses I had then. Big, they was. Weighed 'most a ton each, when they was fat. I loaded a crate of hens in the wagon, an' I tied half-a-dozen hosses to the tail gate. Good hosses, too. It might cost me somethin' to find out what I wanted to know, but I calc'lated it was worth it.

"Wal, sir, this was my plan. I was goin' to ride through the country an' each house I come to, I was goin' to ask the question: Who is the boss here? If the husband ruled the roost, I was goin' to give him his choice of the hosses. If I found out that the wife wore the britches in that house, I was goin' to give her a hen.

"First house I come to," Uncle Ed continued, "there

80

was a feller sittin' on the choppin' block. I asked him the question, tellin' him 'course that I warn't jest bein' curious an' nosey, but that I'd make it right for his time an' information.

" 'Wal,' he says, 'that's the easiest question I ever had to answer. I am the boss, that's who,' he says. 'I make all the decisions around this place.'

"I asked him to pick out the hoss he wanted an' I turned round to untie it. He was a good judge of hoss flesh, that feller was. Picked a little bay, with a white stockin' on his hind leg.

"Jest then a woman come to the door. Sort of a gaunt woman, she was. 'I declare, Homer Johnson,' she says. 'I never knowed a husband like you. You jest get right down to the barn an' feed the pigs. I kin hear em' hollerin'.' She was doing' a little hollerin' herself.

" 'Jest a minute,' he says.

" 'Not another minute!' she screams at him.

" 'But —' he says, tryin' to quiet her until he could git the hoss.

" 'No buts about it,' she hollers, real determined.

" 'Yes, ma'am,' he fin'lly says, an' without another word he turns an' shuffles off to the barn.

"So I tied the hoss back up to the tail gate an' presented the woman with a chicken.

"Next house I come to, there warn't no argument. Both the husband an' the wife agreed that she was the boss.

" 'Yup,' says the feller, 'she wears the britches 'round this place.' So 'course I give 'em a chicken.

"Next house I come to I knocked on the door. I heerd a woman say, 'I'll go to the door, Henry. I can't trust you to speak to strangers. He might be a peddler an' sell you somethin' we ain't got no use for.'

"She come to the door. I tipped my hat as polite as I could. 'Kin I speak to your husband, please?' I says.

" 'What you want?' she says.

"I begun to answer her, but she cut me off. 'You're a peddler, I guess,' she says. I could see her husband trying to look over her shoulder, wantin' to get a word in edgeways.

"I begun to tell her agin, an' she cut me off agin.

" 'Yup. You're a peddler. I kin see that,' she says. 'You're buyin' chickens an' tradin' hosses prob'ly. Wal, my husband don't talk to peddlers.'

" 'But, Marthy,' her husband says. But she cut him off, too, an' kind of shrill, she starts sayin' somethin'. I says, 'Ma'am, please jest stand right there. I want to give you somethin'. I stepped over to the wagon an' got a hen, an' in a minute that woman was standin' there with a squawkin' chicken in her arms an' a be- wildered look on her face.

"Wal, sir, the day wore on, an' I hadn't got rid of a single hoss an' I only had one chicken left. I was gittin' tired. So the next house I come to I asked for a drink of water. Real pleasant people lived there.

Young couple, they was. Quiet speakin' folks, an' the lady was pretty good lookin', too. Had yeller hair.

"We passed the time of day for a minute or so. Then I told 'em. 'I'm conductin' an experiment,' I says. 'An' I'd like to ask you a question.'

" 'What kind of experiment?' he says.

"So I jest told 'em. 'I'm tryin' to find out who wears the pants in a family. You know. Who is the boss? The husband or the wife?'

" 'Wal,' he says, 'I reckon that's a pretty easy question to answer.'

" 'Yup,' she says. 'I guess it is. In this house anyways.'

" 'All right,' I says. 'Who is the boss here? Is it you? Or is it you?'

"She laughed. Real pretty laugh, she had. 'Oh, mercy,' she says. 'I'm not the boss here. Joe is.'

"I turned to him. 'That so?' I asked him.

" 'Yup,' he says. 'I guess it is. I'm the boss here all right, all right.'

" 'All right,' I says. 'You git a hoss.' To tell you the truth, I was kinda glad to git rid of one hoss at last. My mind was almost made up, but it would still be a question seein' that in this house they both agreed that the man wore the pants. They was nice, too, like I said, an' I was glad they was goin' to git a hoss.

" 'Why?' he says. 'Why do I git a hoss?'

"So I told him the whole story. A hoss to the man if he's the boss. A hen to the woman if she's the boss

83

of the family. An' I told 'em I hadn't give a hoss away all day.

" 'It's lucky for us that I'm the boss, ain't it?' he says.

"She agreed with that, you kin bet.

" 'Jest take your pick of the hosses,' I says.

"He looked 'em over real keerful. Fin'lly he says, 'I'll take that bay one there.'

" 'All right,' I says, an' started to untie him.

" 'Oh, Joe,' the lady says. 'Come here a minute, please.'

"Joe turned an' she whispered in his ear. He sort of shook his head an' he whispered back to her. But she whispered agin.

"Fin'lly Joe turned to me an' he says. 'I changed my mind,' he says. 'I'll take that white hoss instead.'

"Wal, I knowed right then who was boss. 'Oh, no you won't,' I says. 'You'll take a chicken.'

"So then my experiment was over. I guess I found out all right who wears the britches in a family. I didn't git rid of even one hoss all day."

The New Camp Stove Burns Again

It was another cool night, and the guests were once again gathered around the fire.

"This would be a good night to have your famous camp stove, Mr. Grant," said one of the guests.

"Yup. 'Twould at that," the Sage of Beaver Pond agreed. "Did I finish tellin' you 'bout that stove?" he asked.

"You told us about the time you put snow on its legs to cool it off."

"But not 'bout the other time?"

"No. Just about the time it got so hot it rose up against the roof and carried the camp up over the woodpile."

"Did something else happen to the stove?"

"Did it? Wal, I should hope to snicker it did."

"What was that, Mr. Grant?"

"Wal, sir, seein' it's you, I'll tell you. It happened the second night I had that stove."

"The second night?"

"Yup. We warn't used to it yet. No, that warn't it. It was because of Mr. Cook.

"I haven't heard of him. He wasn't there the first time you used it, was he?"

"Nope. He come in the next day. The rest of us, we had gone down by the pond to figger 'bout how we could git the camp moved back to where it had been before the new camp stove moved it. Mr. Cook was up in the camp, but fin'lly he come down to where we was, too. We was all talkin' there when all of a sudden I heerd a noise. I looked up an' 'round, an' I see that camp where the new stove was. The smoke was a-comin' out of the chimbly somethin' fierce. It was smokin' like that mountain they got over there in Italy. You know. Vesuvious, I guess it is. 'Course, right off I knowed what had happened. Only thing was, I didn't know how. But that stove was actin' up agin.

" 'The stove!' I yells, pointin' to the camp.

" 'The buckets!' yells Rufe.

"But the buckets was all inside the camp. I turned to Mr. Cook. 'Did you put some wood in that stove?' I asked him.

" 'Why, yes,' he says.

" 'That's what's done it,' I says. 'Come on.'

"They all come with me on the run. As I was runnin' I see we was goin' to have a diff'rent time than we'd had the night before 'cause up there where the camp was carried to the night before when the stove was actin' up, there warn't no snow. First, I thinks, we kin run down the hill to where there is snow. Then, thinks I, I got to find some other way.

"It was quite a predicament, I kin tell you. Here this new man, Mr. Cook, didn't know 'bout that stove — that it had the best draft of any stove in the state o' Maine. An' he'd gone an' put a big load of wood in the stove an' left the draft open. Nature was takin' its course.

"I tell you, nobody could know what that stove might do with a real favorin' draft. I could see as I run along that the stove was a-bumpin' agin the splits in the roof. Too bad, too, 'cause the cold that night had almost taken the swellin' out of 'em from the heat an' the bumpin' they had from the night before.

"I goes in the door, an' what a sight it was! The

damper and the door it was in was wide open, an' there was Missus Stove a-whangin' an' a-bangin' an' a-grumblin' an' a-poppin' an' a-cracklin' an' a-snappin'. She was goin' away like a half-a-dozen donkey engines all workin' at the same time.

"The boys all started huntin' for the buckets an' pans 'cause they was all thinkin' 'bout snow. They had some trouble findin' 'em an' they was bumpin' agin each other, goin' ever' which way like bees a-swarmin'. Fin'lly they was all tryin' to git out of the door at the same time when Rufe, he stopped short an' he says, 'There ain't no snow.'

" 'There's drifts down the hill,' yells John.

" 'We kin git water from the pond,' says Mr. Jackson.

" 'No, we can't,' says one of 'em. 'It's froze.'

"But I was sizin' up the situation an' I see there was only one thing to do. An' it had to be done quick or the stove would bust clean through the roof an' fly to some far place an' we never would find it, havin' a camp with the roof gone, to boot.

"All them fellers was standin' there with empty pails in their hands, 'cept Mr. Cook. He was standin' there with an empty expression on his face. The stove was a-bumpin' and a-bangin' real hard.

" 'Jest take it easy, men,' I says, kinda sharp. That quieted 'em down a little.

" 'It's goin' to burst into flames,' says Mr. Cook.

" 'No, it ain't,' I says. 'Here, Rufe. You an' Elmer

88

help me with this table. Ever'body jest keep calm.'

"They pushed the table up, right under the stove. I got m'self a pair of heavy gloves an' I stood up on the table.

" 'What you goin' to do?' Rufe asked.

" 'Now I got to do this thing easy. Jest right. Not too fast an' not too slow,' I says. They was all watchin' me now, quiet like. It was worse than I thought. Mr. Cook had not only opened the damper, wide open, but he had opened the whole door. I nudged agin the door. Good thing I had some heavy gloves 'cause it was hot, I kin tell you.

"Rufe seen what I was goin' to do. 'Good idee you got there, Ed, shuttin' off the draft,' he says.

" 'Don't close her too fast or she'll drop with a bang,' says Elmer, 'cause he seen what I was about, too.

" 'Course, if I closed her too fast all the draft would be shut off, an' Missus Stove would fall down, flat on her face. An' on me, too, 'cause I was standin' right underneath. It was a pretty ticklish situation. I nudged the door agin. I shut off too much draft all of a sudden, an' the stove lurched sideways an' settled two foot. Jest missed my head, too.

" 'Keerful,' says Rufe.

" 'Too much,' says Elmer.

" 'Slow now,' I says. I closed the door real slow an' steady, shuttin' off the draft gradual like. The air was a-whizzin' past me as it was sucked into the draft. Fin'lly I got the door shut. I figgered that if I could get the draft closed off the stove would settle down to the floor agin. But now the air was roarin' through the open screw damper with a shrill whine, like the Sandy River an' Rangeley Lake Railroad engine as she blowed off steam. There was still enough draft to keep Missus Stove sucked up agin the splits."

"I thought you said the stove had dropped a couple of feet," someone said.

"That's right. So she did," Uncle Ed replied. "But she had worked herself back up to the splits agin.

"This here was the delicate part. One little twist of that screw damper too much, an' down she would come an' very likely bust through the floor, which would of bin almost as bad as bustin' through the roof. Worse, 'cause it would squash me flatter'n a pancake.

"I give her a cautious twist. Oops! She almost fell. 'Easy there, Missus Stove,' thinks I. Then I got her back on an even keel.

"I was turnin' that damper half-a-fraction of an inch this way. Quarter-of-a-fraction that way. The thickness of a frog's hair forward. Back the thickness of the skin of a rock. Nobody said a word. They was quiet, I kin tell you. And down the stove come. She'd slip a little bit sideways. Then she'd stop. She'd start to fall, but a twist of the damper stopped her. Down she come. Slow an' steady.

90

"The noise got shriller as the draft got shut down. Then it started to fade off. I was crouchin' down now. Then I was settin' on the table. Fin'lly I slid off, an' Rufe an' Elmer took the table away. But 'course I couldn't take my eye off the damper. Missus Stove, she'd go up a little. Then she'd go down, but mostly, she come down. Now I was down on my knees. Down she come. Steady.

"Then it was over. The stove was settin' on the floor agin, an' the damper was closed. The fire was burnin' soft, jest like a kitten purrin'. My face was red, an' my whiskers was singed when I stood up. They all let out a sigh of relief you could hear out to Rangeley.

"Mr. Jackson, he turned to Mr. Cook an' he says, 'Harvey,' he says, 'you never should of done that.'

" 'Gorry,' says Mr. Cook. 'How was I to know that stove had such a draft?'

" 'Course he couldn't know, no more'n Mr. Jackson had knowed the night before. But 'course Mr. Jackson forgot he'd done the same thing only the night before.

" 'Good thing you thought of puttin' on the gloves an' turnin' the damper down easy,' says John.

" 'More good things than that,' says Rufe, who had gone to the door.

"I went to the door an' looked out, too. An' d'you know what? That stove had pushed up so hard she had pushed the camp off the ground agin. She'd been flown back right to the spot she was in the day before when she took off the first time!

"Yup. It was true. The camp had got off the ground agin, an' over the woodpile, an' she was back where she started from.

"Mr. Jackson says to me, he says, 'Mr. Grant, d'you know what that stove needs?'

" 'No. What does it need?' says I.

" 'That stove needs a governor,' he says, 'to keep it under control.'

" 'Nope,' says I. 'I'm goin' to bolt her down with iron bolts. Gorry, I don't think a governor could do the job. Matter of fact,' says I, 'I don't think that even the President could hold that stove down!' "

The World's Most Truthful Man

It was quite cool for July, even for northern Maine, and the guests gathered around the fire after supper.

"Mr. Grant," said one of the ladies, "you tell such wonderful stories. Do you ever find anyone who doubts them?"

"Doubts them? No. Why should they?" replied Ed Grant in a puzzled voice.

"Well — some of them are — so — so unusual."

"No, ma'am. I never heerd of anyone ever doubtin' anything I ever said. I guess that's because ever'body knows that I'm jest as honest as a lookin' glass. 'Course I got to admit a lot of curious things have happened to me in my time. But they ain't a bit more curious than they are true."

The Sage of Beaver Pond leaned forward and stirred the fire vigorously. "No. I never like to stretch the truth at all," he continued. "Not even a smidgen. Why, mebby you never heerd about it, but I got quite a reputation for bein' extraordinary honest. I always did make quite a point 'bout tellin' the exact precise truth.

"Matter of fact, I got quite a reputation for truth tellin'. Yup. The Washington family down in Virginny even heerd 'bout it. An' it seems they was so taken by my reputation that they up an' sent me — sort of as an award, y'know — they sent me the very same hatchet that George Washington used when he cut down the cherry tree that time."

"Oh, how wonderful!"

"Yup. Seems like they studied the matter real keer-ful, an' couldn't find no one else that was more de-servin' of it."

"Yes? My, I would like to see it. Where is it now?"

"It's out to Rangeley jest now. An' that's too bad. I meant to bring it up here to the camps, but I plumb forgot 'bout it. I kin tell you I'm real proud of that hatchet. I got to be real keerful of it, though. Y'know how people are, some of 'em anyways, 'bout stealin' tools. They might think it was jest any kind of a hatchet."

The group around the fire was silent. Perhaps the story was not over yet. But, no. The Sage of Beaver Pond gazed into the fire, meditating on his life of honesty, so renowned that he had been presented with the country's most famous symbol of perfect truthfulness.

One of the guests stirred. "Goodness, it's real cold tonight, isn't it?"

"Yup. It sure is. But not as cold as one night I remember," said Uncle Ed.

"How's that?" Perhaps there *would* be another tale.

"Yes. Tell us about it, Mr. Grant."

"Wal, sir, seein' it's you. It's a time I won't never forgit, I kin tell you," said the old man. "But speakin' of honesty an' truthfulness an' such things, an' then the cold night, too, it sort of brings to mind an experience I had once. Mebby you'd like to hear 'bout it," he added, apparently forgetting the recent request.

"Yes."

"Oh, yes."

Uncle Ed paused. A long pause. "Wal, sir, it was a long time ago. I had jest started these camps then. Must of been 'bout the first year. No. Mebby the second season. Yup. That was it. The second season. Jest afterwards. I was out trappin' after the season was over.

The weather was pretty good, an' I didn't expect no storm nor nothin'. An' I'm pretty good 'bout bein' able to tell 'bout the weather, too. But in the early days I made mistakes now an' then. Still do, for that matter. Once in a while. Feller can't be perfect all the time. Yup. This time I made a real mistake. A humdinger, you might say. The storm come up quick, so I made me a lean-to."

"A what?" a lady asked.

"A lean-to," her husband said helpfully. "A shelter."

"Yup. That's what I said, a lean-to," the Sage agreed. "An' I used to make a real good lean-to, if I do say so m'self. But this time, I didn't have very much time. An' the storm was real bad, like I say. Yup. Real bad. It rained, an' the rain turned into sleet, an' the sleet an' rain froze on the lean-to. It was real heavy, an' all of a sudden, she started crackin'. It prob'ly would of held up, though, but a limb hangin' overhead busted. *Crack*, she went, an' down she come, right on top of my lean-to."

Uncle Ed got up and poked the fire deliberately and carefully. "You got to know how, an' do it jest so, to keep a fire burnin' jest right," he said as he returned to his chair and comfortably seated himself.

"Let's see now. Where was I?" he asked.

"A limb fell on your lean-to," someone said.

"Oh, yup. That's right. Wal, sir, I had to find me somewheres to go. The sleet had turned to rain agin.

96

The fire was doused by the sleet an' water, an' my shelter was gone."

"What did you do?"

"I was lucky. Don't know what might of happened otherwise, but there was a big ol' log there. An' it was holler. Good, thinks I. This holler log is jest the ticket. So in I crawled. It was kinda snug, but I was out of the weather in there, an' I goes to sleep.

"Wal, sir, I was kinda tuckered out, bein' woke up in the night when my lean-to was broke down. So I had my sleep out. By the time I woke up, the sun was shinin' nice an' warm. I could see that out of the end of the holler log.

"An' there was somethin' else I noticed, too." The old gentleman paused. The question was on everyone's lips. It was in the air. But the only sound was the crackling fire.

"By gorry, I noticed that the log didn't fit me nice an' snug no more. It was tight. That's what it was. Yup. It was tight. Downright tight."

"What was the matter?"

"What happened?"

"What happened? I'll tell you what happened. The sun had come up bright an' warm. Warm for a cold day, that is. An' it struck agin that holler log, an' the log had commenced to shrink. You know how wood does. If I had woke up ten, mebby fifteen minutes earlier, I could of got out before it had shrunk so

97

much. But I didn't. An' there I was, held tight. Like a foot in a new shoe. Only there warn't no way to git out. I could feel that holler log shrinkin' in on me. An' I could hear it sort of creakin' as it shrunk. *Crick. Creak. Crick,* it went.

"Tight as it was, it was gettin' still tighter. I couldn't move no ways. Couldn't move my arms. Couldn't move my hands. I couldn't even move my ankles nor my feet. I could jest sort of see the open end of that holler log out of the corner of one eye when I turned my eyes jest so. But I could see that the hole was gittin' smaller an' smaller, an' I knowed that pretty soon, I wouldn't have enough room to move even my eyeballs."

The old man paused. "I was stuck in there tighter than cucumber pickles in a jar." He reflected for a moment. "Yup. Tighter than lead in a lead pencil.

There was another pause. "It was pretty desperate, I kin tell you." He nodded thoughtfully as his mind went back to review the obviously uncomfortable and dangerous moment.

"Whatever did you do, Mr. Grant?"

"Wal, sir. Do y'know what people do when their end is near? Like when they are drownin', and' goin' down for the last time?"

"I've heard that in that last moment their whole life passes before them."

"That's right, an' you heerd right. That's what

happened to me. I can't tell you how many things I thought of."

"They say it's the bad things that come to mind."

"Yup. Right agin. Only right away it come to me that I warn't thinkin' so much 'bout m'self. 'Course, I don't lay claim that I never done no bad things. It wouldn't sound modest for me to say such a thing. But it is a fact, nonetheless, that I couldn't think of a single bad thing I'd ever done so as I could feel repentful. Thinks I, mebby I done some bad thing without knowin' it. But nope. I couldn't think of a single one. But, do y'know what I did think of?"

"No. What?"

"I thought of the bad things other people had done. An' all of a sudden I was thinkin' 'bout Rufe Crosby an' Dick Huntoon an' John Meader, an' all them other guides. An' I thought of all them stories they used to tell. Then all at once it dawned on me that people used to believe them stories, an' that they warn't nothin' but lies. Yarns, y'might say. Tall tales, stretchin' the blanket, drawin' the long bow.

"An' not only did it dawn on me that other people believed them yarns, but that I had believed them, too. Natur'lly, 'course I believed them 'cause I never could see how anybody could lie or even wander away from the honest, strict truth.

"Wal, sir, when I realized that, I certainly started to feel pretty small. Jest to think that I believed all

99

them tales they told. The more I thought 'bout it, the smaller I felt. Felt no bigger'n a six-year-old hick'ry tree. Then, pretty soon I felt as small as an axe helve. An' that's when I done it."

"What did you do?"

"Yes. Did what?"

"Why, since I was feelin' so small, I jest crawled right out of that holler log as quick as I could, an' I didn't have no trouble at all. I guess that was 'bout the narrowest escape I ever had."

Maine's Best Boatman

Dinner was over. The sun was high in the sky, pausing after its long morning climb to the zenith before sliding down half a hemisphere of cloud-flecked blue to the pine-pointed hills in the west. Eager little waves spread out in the wake of a rowboat on the lake and shimmered out of sight in the smooth surface.

The memory of a fine dinner gave way to words.

101

"I suppose there are a lot of excellent boatmen around Rangeley," someone said.

"I should think there would be," another guest responded. "All this water, you know."

"Yup," Mr. Grant said. "I calc'late we have some of the finest boatmen here in the Rangeley district as a body is likely to find anywheres."

"Who would you say is the best boatman, Mr. Grant?"

The party had been walking slowly toward the chairs in the sun-splashed shade of the pines at the water's edge. Ed Grant reached a chair. He was thoughtful.

"The best boatman in these parts, hey?" he mused. "That's a pretty difficult question. There is lots of guides round here an' most of 'em is pretty handy with a boat. Sometime back Corneil Richardson was 'bout as good as any, I always thought. An' folks has said that I warn't no slouch, either. Out of my hearin', of course. Yup. Pole, oars or paddle, people used to say that I was 'bout the best. 'Course I never really claimed to be what you might call the best. But you can't help what people say 'bout you. As long as it's true, I guess it don't really make no diff'rence."

The old gentleman paused. "Now that you mention it," he said, " 'bout boat rowin' an' all, I mind one time that you might like to hear 'bout."

"Yes. What was it?"

It was an invitation eagerly given and soberly re-

ceived. Uncle Ed eased down in his chair and reached
for his pipe. The guests edged their own chairs into
good positions and waited patiently, but eagerly, for
the deliberate words that would be punctuated with
equally deliberate processes of cleaning, loading, lighting and relighting the ancient, black pipe.

"It was a good time back. I was a young feller then.
Pretty strong, too, as I was doin' a good day's work
ever' day, runnin' trap lines in the winter, y'know.
Many's the load I toted back from the Canada border.
Real loads, too.

"Wal, sir, a couple of young fellers was stoppin'
down to Mountain View. They was from some big college as I rec'lect, an' they had a little boat. A cedar
boat, it was. An' trim, too. Built for speed. They was
practicin' for some college athletics. Trainin', y'know.
They rowed it round pretty fast. They was strong
young bucks, an' they had the idee they was *it*. You
could jest see it stickin' out all over 'em. They thought
they were some punkins, I kin tell you.

"Seems like they warn't satisfied havin' that fast boat.
Cedar, it was, an' a real pretty little boat. An' bein'
they was real good at rowin' it, they used to go 'round
talkin' 'bout how fast they could row. An' they could,
too. Make no mistake 'bout it. 'Course they was young
bucks. Strong.

"One of 'em, name of Hardy, or mebby it was
Harvey. I don't rec'lect jest which it was now. But his

name ain't important. No. Now that I think of it, his name was Hardy. Yup. That's it, Hardy.

"Wal, sir, he come right out an' he wanted to bet me. He'd heerd somehow that I was the best boatman round Rangeley. The guides and folks talk 'bout a person that happens to be pretty good at doin' somethin', y'know. I guess he must of heerd right, 'cause he didn't want to run no even race. But he had a lot of gall. He says to me, he'd bet me a ten dollar bill that him an' his partner could beat me in a boat race, providin' I'd give 'em five minutes head start.

" 'Course, I ain't a bettin' man an' I told him so. But I surmised as how I wouldn't mind a rowin' match anyway. A Rangeley man don't feel right if he don't accept a challenge like that.

"Two, three guides was there. Amos Ellis, Al Sprague, an' mebby some more, an' they knowed somethin' 'bout my rowin', so they got up some cash. I don't like to have folks bet on me, 'cause I might jest accident'lly lose. Somethin' might happen, y'know. If it did, they might feel bad if they had to lose.

" 'Fore I knowed it, them young fellers got in that slick little boat an' away they went. Me, I didn't even have a boat yet, but I see one over yonder. It was a heavy scow that had a square end. It leaked more'n a little bit. I didn't much like the looks of the boat, but there warn't nothin' else, so I gets in her.

" 'Course, by that time them two young fellers was

104

quite a piece away, an' they was goin' at a good clip. Says I, 'Ed Grant, you have got yourself quite a job here,' an' off I started.

"The folks on the shore, they give a cheer. 'Course, it warn't long till I edged up to them two young fellers in that pretty little cedar boat. They was makin' good time. Like I say, they had been practicin' ever' day. But I was young an' strong, too, an' soon as I got goin', I went past them jest like they was standin' still. Lickity split.

"I had 'em beat for sure, providin', of course, nothin' happened, an' a body never knows what might happen in a boat race. 'But,' thinks I, 'I'll jest settle down to some real serious rowin' an' make a new record for Rangeley Lake.' Quite a crowd was there, like I say, an' I was ready to show 'em some real rowin'.

"Wal, sir, I didn't know a boat could go that fast. I was a-flyin', I kin tell you. 'Twarn't long 'fore I see that the water splashin' 'round in the boat started to steam. Like I said, it was a leaky boat. Then I see that the wood was a-startin' to smoke 'round the edges at the water line. It was the friction, y'know, goin' along through the water so fast.

"My hand was tough 'cause, like I say, I was workin' steady then, but the oars started gittin' hot to my hands. If that warn't enough, the soles of my shoes begun to burn from touchin' the bottom of the boat which was gittin' hotter n' hotter all the time.

105

"I looked back at the wake I was makin'. There was a cloud of steam risin' after me an', by gorry, I see little white dots a-floatin' in the wake. Lots of 'em. Wal, now, I couldn't figger out what they was, but there warn't no time for that, anyway. I was in danger, bein' in that burnin' boat, an' all. She might jest bust into flame any minute.

"I looked at the oars. They warn't nothin' but a couple of sticks. The blades was all wore off an' they was smokin' at the oarlocks.

"It was gettin' pretty desperate. I never looked for anything like that. It kinda looked like I might have a watery grave an' that I'd perish in a burnin' boat on Rangeley Lake.

"But, by gorry, I couldn't stop then. Them two young bucks was lost way back yonder in the steam I was leavin', but I give her all I had an' run her up on the beach an' jumped out like a cat jumpin' away from a dog fight.

" 'Twarn't a minute too soon. The boat busted into flames before my eyes, an' quicker than you could say *Jack Robinson,* she was nothin' but a pile of ashes. Lost my coat an' hat, too, 'cause I didn't have time to git 'em out."

"What happened to the boys, Mr. Grant?"

"Oh, them? I never saw 'em agin. Someone told me that they went back to the hotel, an' the next day they was gone."

106

"Those white spots, Mr. Grant. What were they?"

"Hey? What's that?" the Sage of Beaver Pond asked.

"The white spots. The dots, you know. They bobbed up back of the boat. What were they?"

"Them? Oh, wal, I 'most forgot 'bout them. Wal, that was mighty curious. Al Sprague come along in his boat, follerin' me, an' he sees 'em. He wondered what they was, so he scooped up a pail full. Yup. That was curious. They was fish, that's what they were. An' they was boiled. All boiled white. We et 'em right then an' there. They was real tasty, too. Never tasted better cooked fish. Must of bin because they was cooked so fast."

Ed Grant Out West

"Y up," said Uncle Ed Grant. "All the young 'uns nowadays want to be cowboys. Don't know as I blame 'em. I used to want to be a cowboy m'self."

"Oh," said one of the guests. "I thought you were a real Maine man, Mr. Grant."

"So I am. A real dyed-in-the-wool State o' Mainer. But still, I hankered after bein' a cowboy when I was

young, an' I went out West to do it. An' I might jest
as well tell you 'bout a mistake I made when I was
out West. It was a terrible mistake, too. I don't usually talk 'bout it. 'Course I don't often make mistakes.
Never did. But I have made a few in my time. An'
this partic'lar one was what you might call a humdinger."

The Sage of Beaver Pond was about to tell a tale.
The folks on the porch came to attention. No detail
of one of Ed Grant's yarns should be missed.

"Wal, sir, I made my way out to Montana, an' now
that I think back on it, I can't imagine a more un-
likely candidate for cow punchin'. Fin'lly I got to a
little place out there. I was low on funds, an' I needed
a job. Needed it bad.

"Did you ever stop to think 'bout it? First thing a
feller needs, no matter where he is, is a job. 'Less he's
got money, 'course. Don't make no diff'rence if you're
in the State o' Maine or the State o' Montana. But I
found I warn't in the cow country. I was in the sheep
country. But that didn't make no diff'rence neither.
I was young an' strong an' willin' to work, an' so this
sheep rancher loads me in his wagon an' off we goes.

"Fin'lly, we git to the ranch. An ol' sheep herder
had jest come in off the range. He'd bin out there
alone, with nothin' but sheep for company for so long
he'd 'most forgot how to talk. An' if he warn't keer-

110

ful, he'd say *baa* for *yes* or *no* when you was talkin'
to him. You got no idee how lonesome it kin get when
you're out on the prairie alone for months at a time
with nothin' but sheep to talk to."

Uncle Ed scratched his beard thoughtfully. "Don't
know as I'd remember how to talk sheep language
any more. I might if I had some Montana sheep to
talk to.

"But that ain't what I was tellin' you. I was tellin'
you 'bout a mistake I once made, warn't I?"

"Yes, Mr. Grant."

"Let's see. Oh, yes. Wal, sir, that first night, jest
'fore the sun went down, it was. Must of bin a couple
of hours of daylight left. The boss asked me to go out
west of the ranch house in some low-lyin' hills an'
bring in the sheep that was out there.

"I was on the jump. I had gone out to Montana to
make my fortune, an' this was my first job. I was determined I was goin' to do it right, even if it was
chasin' sheep instead of punchin' cows, which is what
I went out there for in the first place.

"The boss says to me, 'Now don't go an' git lost,
m'boy.'

"I says I wouldn't, 'course.

"An' he says, 'Be sure you git all them sheep rounded
up, 'cause there is coyotes out there an' they will kill
any that's left behind.'

111

"An' I says, 'I'll git 'em all. Don't worry.'

"Wal, sir, I never had such a time, I kin tell you. I always was a pretty good runner, an' 'course I knowed 'bout sheep 'cause we had 'em back in Maine. But it warn't long 'fore I realized I didn't know 'bout them Montana sheep. They was wild. I never seen critters that could run like they could.

"The sun slid down an' the moon popped up over them mountains. An' they really got mountains out there in Montana. Like I say, I never seen such sheep before, an' I never seen such mountains neither. I was still goin' after them sheep an' lambs. Them lambs was a caution. Run! I never seen critters run like they could. But, like I say, I was always a good runner m'self an', thinks I, if they want to run, I'll run after 'em.

"Fin'lly, I got 'em in to the corral. Hazed 'em in, like they used to say out in Montana. I got ever' last one of 'em in, an' the gate locked tight.

"Then the boss come up. Seems like he got to worryin' 'bout me, an' when he seen I hadn't got back, he went out to look for me.

" 'Wal,' he says, 'I was worryin' 'bout you.'

" 'No need for that,' says I. Though, to tell the truth, I had bin a little worried once in a while when I was chasin' them lambs out over them hills. Y'know, there ain't no trees nor landmarks of no kind out there like we got here in Maine. But I had noticed where the sun went down an' where the moon come up, so I warn't lost.

" 'Did you get 'em?' the boss asked.

"I says, 'Yup.'

" 'Did y'have any trouble?' he says.

" 'No,' I says. 'I didn't have no trouble with the sheep, but the lambs was some trouble an' could run like blazes.'

" 'Lambs?' says he. 'There ain't no lambs.'

" 'Yup,' says I. 'There *is* lambs. Eleven lambs. Eleven lambs an' two hundred an' twenty-seven sheep.'

" 'Let's see them lambs,' says he.

" 'Come on,' says I, an' we walked along. 'There's the sheep,' I says, pointin' to 'em as they skittered out of reach.

" 'Yup,' he says. 'Where's the lambs?'

" 'Right over here,' says I as I took him to the far corner of the corral. 'They're kind of tuckered out from runnin', but ever' single one I seen is here. An' none of 'em is left out in the pasture for the coyotes to git.'

"He goes with me, an' there they was all huddled up together in the corner of the corral. The moon was up bright now. The moon is usually pretty bright out in Montana. Wal, sir, he looks at them critters in the corner an' he lets out a gasp.

" 'M'boy,' he says. 'Them ain't lambs. Them is jack rabbits!' "

113

The old man turned to his listeners. "An' that's the mistake I made out in Montana. I had corralled eleven Montana jack rabbits, thinkin' they was lambs. By gorry! They didn't look like no rabbits I ever seen. Nothin' like our cotton tails an' snowshoe rabbits. 'Course, they didn't look much like our State o' Maine lambs neither. But lots of things was diff'rent out in Montana, an' I figgered I shouldn't take no chance, what with him tellin' me 'bout the coyotes an' all.

"To this day, I think jack rabbits look more like lambs than like snowshoe rabbits, or any other rabbits, for that matter.

"Like I told you before, I was a pretty fast runner when I was young, in the early days. An' I guess that proves I was some runner, don't it? It stands to reason that anyone who could corral all them jack rabbits like that must of bin pretty fast on his feet."

114

An Adventure with a Bear

"I reckon I've had to do with bears more'n most people," said the Sage of Beaver Pond.

Uncle Ed Grant was going to tell a story, and his audience gave close and respectful attention. No one wanted to miss a word.

"Yes, sir, an' one time the most peculiar thing happened to me that I guess ever happened to anybody. With a bear, that is.

"It was in the early days. Must of bin 'bout the first season me an' Rufe trapped together. No. 'Twarn't. It was the second season. That would make it 'bout 1867. Rufe was a good man to go partners with. None better. We run traps from Rangeley north to the Canada border.

"It was close to the end of the season. We was 'bout ready to go out to Rangeley. I was workin' on a farm in the summertime, down to Natick, in them days. That's in Massachusetts. Down near Boston.

"Wal, sir, it happened when I was comin' down to Beaver Pond from Little Island Pond. I was a-comin' down the trail. It was 'bout dusk. Then all of a sudden I see this bear. 'Course, 'twarn't nothin' unusual to see a bear in them days. But this bear was kinda grumpy. No, that ain't quite right. He was real grumpy. Matter of fact, he was mad, as I soon found out. I warn't interested in him, but he showed considerable interest in me. He jest came at me kinda crazy like. Jest took one look at me, mind you. Then he come at me, his eyes a-shinin' like new money."

"What did you do?" a listener asked.

"Goodness!" exclaimed another.

"What did I do?" repeated Uncle Ed. "Why, I turned real quick, gittin' ready to run. An' gorry! I stumbled over a rock. When I went down, my gun somehow got on the other side of some alders an' as I fell, I lost it."

"Lost your gun?"

"Yup. It got mixed up in them alder branches. My hold on it was broke, an' there I was, kind of on one knee an' with no gun in my hand.

"Mister Bear was comin' an' he was comin' fast, an' he didn't have much further to come. Wal, sir, seein' as how I didn't have no hankerin' to be a bear's breakfast, I got to my feet as fast as I could an' lit out of there.

"But I found out that when I fell I had turned my ankle. It warn't hurt real bad. Jest a little. But it slowed me down. Wal, sir, this bear was both mad an' hungry, an' he was 'most right up on top of me. I could feel his hot breath on the back of my neck. Did you ever have that feelin'?"

"No, thank goodness," breathed the listeners.

"Stay away from it as long as you kin. It's real unpleasant. Wal, sir, he was goin' to ketch me, so I figgered I had to do somethin' diff'rent. Anything. So I done it."

"What?"

"Yes. What did you do?"

"I turned right 'round an' I faced Mister Bear an' I give him a punch in the snoot, that's what I done.

"It helped some. He stopped. But then he got madder or hungrier, I couldn't tell which. But I don't suppose it really makes any diff'rence. It give me some time, an' I turned an' run agin. I looks over my shoulder, an' there was Mister Bear, comin' like sixty. I could see he was ketchin' up with me agin. I always was a pretty fast runner, but my ankle was holdin' me down.

"Then, pretty soon, I didn't need to look back, for I could feel that hot breath on the back of my neck agin. So I says to m'self, says I, 'I'll give that bear a smack on the nose he won't soon forget.' There warn't nothin' else to do. Not that I could think of anyways.

"So I turned quick an' doubles up my fist agin' an' I aimed straight for his snoot agin. It would of hurt him, too, only —"

"Only what, Mr. Grant?"

Uncle Ed stuffed his pipe carefully and tamped the contents down neatly at the edges of the bowl. His listeners waited until he had finished.

"Let's see, where was I?" the old man asked.

"You aimed at his nose again."

"Oh, yes. Like I say, it would of hurt him, too, only jest at that minute he opened his mouth. Wide. I guess he must of thought he was close enough to take a bite out of me. Or mebby he was jest pantin', for we had been runnin' quite a piece. Wal, he was comin' fast, an' his mouth was open, so when I went to hit him, I jest rammed my fist right down his throat."

The Sage of Beaver Pond paused. "Anybody got a match?" he asked.

"Yes, here's one."

He took the match, saying, "Thank you. Don't ever

seem to have enough matches." He lit it and held it while he attended to some small grains of tobacco by pressing his big thumb down firmly on top of the black bowl. He held the almost-devoured match to it, and took a couple of small puffs before it went out. Then, holding the pipe in one hand and the burned-out match in the other, he continued.

"Let's see — " he said.

"You had rammed your fist down the bear's throat," someone offered.

"Oh, yes. Wal, when I say rammed, I mean rammed, for my arm went clean in up to the shoulder. I was hittin' at him hard, y'remember. I didn't have time hardly to think 'bout it. An' it's a good thing, too, for jest then my hand hit somethin' hard.

"It was his tail. My hand had hit his tail. An' before I knowed it, I had hold of Mister Bear's tail, from the inside. I give it a pull. A good firm pull, an' I jest pulled Mister Bear inside out.

"Now, natur'lly, when he was pulled inside out, instead of his runnin' towards me, he was runnin' away from me. Y'know, before I seen it, I never thought to puzzle about that, but that's what happened. An' a body kin see that that would be the case. If he was outside out an' inside in when he was runnin' towards me, it stands to reason he'd be runnin' away from me when he was inside out an' outside in. His front would be in the rear, an' his rear would be in the front.

"The bear must of changed his mind, jest like he changed his direction, an' the last I see of him, he was lopin' over the hill an' lookin' like he was peeled clean as a skinned grape."

Uncle Ed paused again and applied a fresh match to his pipe as he contemplated the strange adventure with the bear.

"An', d'you know, that ain't all," he finally said. "Somehow — an' to save me, I don't exactly know jest how, 'cause it all happened so fast — I was standin' there with 'bout half of a bear liver in my hand.

"The way I always figgered that out was that I guess I must of put my other hand up to push when I was pullin' my hand out that had hold of the tail. There was stresses an' strains in ever' direction at the time, so I suppose I pushed against his liver as I was pullin' him inside out. An' in the excitement an' the hurry an' all, I somehow got hold of half of his liver an' didn't let go when he started to run in the other direction.

"We had that half of liver for breakfast, an' I declare, I don't believe Rufe would ever have believed what had happened if I hadn't had the liver to prove it."

A Most Peculiar Bear Hide

"**D**id you ever have any more adventures with bears, Mr. Grant?"

"Wal, yes, as a matter of fact, I did. I've had lots to do with bears in my day," said the Sage of Beaver Pond. "Have I ever told you 'bout the bear I turned inside out?"

"Yes. You told us about that."

121

"When he went a-runnin' away, with his hide on the inside?"

"Yes."

"Wal, then I might jest as well tell you 'bout another experience I had, seein' it's you.

"It happened after Rufe an' I first went out trappin' as partners. We must of bin together three or four years. We had bin runnin' trap lines as far north as Canada. We come back here to Beaver Pond, jest gittin' ready to go out to Rangeley.

"Then one day, Rufe come a-runnin' down the path yellin'. I couldn't make out what he was sayin' at first, an' when I met him, 'course I asked him what was the matter.

" 'Come! Come quick!' That was all he could say. He hurried down the path, an' me beside him tryin' to find out what was the matter. But all I could git out of him was, 'Never, never, never have I seen anything like it.' He was pretty excited 'bout somethin', I kin tell you.

" 'Man an' boy,' he says, 'as man and boy I have hunted an' trapped, but I can't believe it.'

" 'Can't believe what?' I says. But I couldn't git nothin' out of him.

"Pretty soon we come to a place where there was a bear trap and a bear. Rufe had already started to skin him, but he hadn't finished.

" 'Look!' he says, pointin' at it, actin' 'bout like an

actor who was actin' a Shakespeare play. 'Look!' he says.

"I looked, but I didn't see nothin' but a bear that he'd jest started to skin.

" 'I see a bear,' " I says. 'What is it I'm supposed to see?'

"For the first time since he'd started yellin', Rufe kinda simmered down. Then he got real solemn an' he turned to me an' he says, 'This bear has two hides.' His voice was solemn, but it was throbbin' some, 'most like he was skeered to say what he was sayin'.

" 'Two hides?' I says, figgerin' that mebby I didn't hear him right.

" 'Yup.' he says. But he couldn't seem to say no more words.

"Soon as I was sure I was hearin' him right, I says, 'Let's go take a look.'

"We started over to Mister Bear, an' Rufe found his tongue agin, an' the words tumbled out of his mouth.

" 'Yup, it's true,' he says. 'He was in the trap. I shot him an' then I started to skin him. First off, I run into the second hide. I got muddled, kinda. Never skinned a bear with two hides before,' he says. 'So I come to camp for you. You kin see for yourself,' he says.

"When I got up to the bear, I started in to examine him, an' git ready to finish skinnin' him, an' by gorry, d'you know, Rufe was right. That critter did have two hides. There was one on the inside an' there was one

on the outside. Look down his mouth an' there was
fur on the inside.

"Rufe, he says, 'I don't see how such a thing could be.'

" 'Course I didn't neither. But then I got to figgerin'.

" 'Jest a minute,' I says. 'Now that I see it, I think
I know what has happened.'

"An' the more I figgered on it, the more sure I was
that I knowed how it come about. 'This must be the
same bear I turned inside out last year,' I says.

" 'No!' he says.

" 'Yup,' says I. 'Look here. Here is the scar on his
nose where I punched him. An' here. His tail is sort
of twisted. Jest like it would be if it was pulled inside
out. I rec'lect I had a good firm hold on that tail.'

"We kep' on a-workin' there. Fin'lly I see that the
bear only had half a liver.

" 'Look,' I says. 'He's only got half of a liver. That's
because we had the other half for breakfast last year.'

" 'By gorry,' Rufe says. 'I guess you're right.'

" ' 'Course I'm right,' I says. An' I was, too.

"By gorry, I never seen a bear like that before, or
since, for that matter. A bear with a skin on the inside and a bear skin on the outside, too.

"When I had turned that bear inside out, his hide —
that is, his outside hide — was on the inside. Then he
went an' growed another bear hide on the outside,
which was really his inside, so then his outside hide

124

was on the inside an' his inside had a hide on the outside.

"An' we had had the other half of the liver for break-fast. It was real good, that liver was. Must of had somethin' to do with its bein' turned inside out, I always figgered.

"But anyways, that's how that bear come to have two hides. I always thought it was real curious. Yup. Real curious."

Some Punkins

"My, your vegetable garden looks nice, Mr. Grant," one of the ladies said.

"I should say so. I was noticing it this morning," another added.

"Wal, we got to raise our own vegetables, bein' out here at Beaver Pond so far from Rangeley," Uncle Ed replied.

"The soil must be pretty good up here."

"Yup. Guess there ain't soil much better in the whole country," Uncle Ed agreed. "Gits kinda dangerous sometimes though."

"Dangerous? How is that?"

"Wal, it ain't that way so much any more, but it certainly used to be. That is, if everythin' was jest right in the spring. The right kind of rain, an' all. Then, too, the seed has got to be right, too. Why, I mind once I sent one of the boys down to plant corn. He warn't gone long when I hear him yellin' like blazes. I went out to the back of the camp and looked over to the garden an' I see him fallin' down in a most unaccountable way. Then, he'd git up an' pretty soon he'd fall down agin.

"Didn't take me but a minute to know what was happenin', after I considered it. So I run down to help him. Then 'course it was all right."

"What was all right?"

"Yes. What was happening?"

"Wal, he was leanin' over to put the corn in the ground. He got it planted all right, but then he didn't git out of the way."

"Out of the way of what?"

"Why, of the corn, of course," the old man replied. "Soon as he got the corn in the ground an' covered over, it started growin'. An' up it popped. Growed so fast it jest popped right up an' hit him. Like I say, he was bendin' right over it an' he didn't git out of the way in time. 'Course ever'thing was jest right that year. The seed, an' soil, an' all."

"My!" one of the ladies exclaimed.

"Did anything else like that ever happen?"

The Sage of Beaver Pond took out his pipe and blew through it as he pondered the question. Taking out his tobacco, he proceeded methodically to load the pipe, using great care to see that it was packed just right. This done, he rubbed the dark bowl slowly. The guests knew, or hoped, that this was the prelude to a story. Would another tall tale appear? Yes, it would.

"Yup. Some real curious things has happened up here that has had to do with vegetables."

"What were they, Uncle Ed?"

The old man produced a match and lit it. "Wal, sir, seein' it's you, I'll tell you."

Match in one hand, pipe in the other, he said, "Take punkins, for instance. I rec'lect a real curious thing happened 'bout them once. 'Course they growed fast, too. The vines growed so fast they'd run you down if you warn't keerful. Lost a lot of punkins 'count of their growin' so fast."

"How was that?"

Uncle Ed blew the match out just as it seemed sure to burn his fingers, then replied. "The vines growed so fast they wore out a lot of punkins by draggin' 'em across the ground.

"One year the punkins did real good. The vines

129

growed so fast I could see somethin' would have to be done, so I trained 'em to grow back an' forth from the garden across that little neck of the pond there. I guided the first one across the pond an' turned it 'round a tree. Then I turned it 'round another tree on this side, an' back and forth they growed. Back an' forth. They kep' on growin' an' made a regular bridge 'cross the water. A man could walk on them vines, they was that thick. Made quite a bridge. I've heerd of bridges made out of vines in lots of places in the world. But they ain't punkin vines.

" 'Long towards the end of the season I went out to Rangeley. Ever'body else had gone and I intended to come back. I had to come back 'cause I had an old sow an' a few shoats up here at Beaver Pond that I had to take keer of.

"But it snowed early that year. I hadn't harvested the punkins yet either. Had a real good stand, too." There was pause. "Anybody got a match?"

A match was produced, and the Sage struck it. After a longer pause, he touched it to the tobacco and puffed noisily until the flame reached a point dangerous to his thumb. He blew the flame out just in time to prevent the impending tragedy.

"Let's see. Where was I?"

"You had to go to Rangeley."

"And leave the pigs."

"Oh, yes. Wal, it snowed early that year. An' hard. An' I took down with a bad cold. I don't often git a

130

cold, but I sure had one that year, I kin tell you.
Bad one.

"So I couldn't git back to Beaver Pond. In the early
days a little thing like a blizzard wouldn't of stopped
me. I'd of come up on snowshoes for them pigs. I always figger that if a body has animals, it's up to him
to take keer of 'em. 'Tain't right not to. 'Course lots
of animals kin take pretty good keer of themselves.
But, like I say, one thing an' another kep' happenin'
an' I didn't git back to the camps till after high water
the follerin' spring.

"'When I fin'lly got back I certainly figgered I had
lost them pigs. Nice shoats they was, too, an' I felt
terrible 'bout that sow. Red, she was.

"I no more'n got here when I heerd a terrible lot
of squealin'. I couldn't scarcely believe my ears. Wal,
thinks I, that squealin' sounds like pigs. How could
that be? I didn't think pigs could live through a hard
winter like we'd had without someone takin' keer
of 'em.

"I started to look 'round, tryin' to make out where
the noise was comin' from. There warn't no pigs 'round
the camp nowheres. Then I see where the squealin'
was comin' from. It was comin' from 'cross that little
neck of water. I went down there an' I look an' by
gorry, there them pigs was 'cross the water.

"I couldn't see how it happened, 'cause a pig won't
usually swim. Then I knowed what had happened.
Thinks I, them pigs et up all the punkins on this side

an' they went across on that bridge of punkin vines.

"I went over there as quick as I could, an' what d'you suppose I found?"

"I can't imagine."

"Nor I."

"What did you find, Uncle Ed?"

"I found ever' one of them shoats was safe an' sound. Ever' pig had growed considerable. Jest as sassy an' fat as you please. An' the old sow had a new litter of nine pigs that was jest as nice as any you'd ever want to see.

"I puzzled 'bout it for a minute as to how they'd done it. Then I see what had happened. The punkins that had growed on that side was 'bout as big as a wagon box. Them pigs had each et their way into a punkin an' had stayed there all winter. Out of the cold an' munchin' away on nice, fresh punkin whenever they got hungry. The old sow had et her way into the biggest punkin and had raised a whole litter of pigs in there. They was all fat an' strong an' gittin' along fine. Jest as comfortable as bugs in a rug."

Uncle Ed struck another match. He held it at the waiting bowl of his pipe and puffed until the flame went out. He paused for a long moment. Then he knocked the unburned tobacco out and returned the pipe to his pocket.

"I don't rec'lect we have had any punkins that big since that time," he said. "They was some punkins."

A Curious Tale

"**D**oesn't the cold do a lot of damage up here in the wintertime, Uncle Ed?" one of the men asked.

"But you must have good skating, though," commented another.

"Both of them things is true," Ed Grant replied. "We have good skatin' an' the cold does do damage. I call to mind a real curious thing that happened once.

You mentionin' skatin' an' the cold an' all brings it back. I hadn't thought of it for a long time now."

"What was that, Uncle Ed?"

"Wal, sir, seein' it's you, I'll tell you. I got to tell you, though, the ladies might not be able to stand it."

"Oh, we can stand it, all right, Mr. Grant," one of the ladies hurriedly assured him.

"Oh, yes, Mr. Grant. Tell us," another added.

"Wal, if you say so. But don't say I didn't warn you. It ain't like nothin' you prob'ly ever heerd 'bout before."

"Please tell us," another added warmly.

The Sage of Beaver Pond wrapped his fingers around the black bowl of his pipe, and rubbed it fondly. Everyone waited expectantly. The silence was almost tangible.

Uncle Ed began slowly to fill his pipe. "It was a cold day," he said, "an' this here feller was skatin'. Havin' a wonderful time. Good skater, he was, though I thought he was a little bit too old to be skatin'. Y'know, when a person gits old, he might break a bone in a fall. Young folks kin take a fall, but when a person gits up in years, he shouldn't risk it.

"Like I say, it was cold. Cold as a polar bear's nose. But notwithstandin', there was a hole in the ice. I was right nearby, comin' back from huntin', I was. I see this hole in the ice, an' I knowed somethin' was goin' to happen, 'cause this feller was cuttin' up a lot of didoes on the ice an' not watchin' where he was goin'. But it was too late for me to do anything by the time I see what was goin' to happen, even though I warn't more'n twenty feet away."

He struck a match for his pipe and held it while the flame grew. "Then *zip* that feller fell in the hole with a splash," he continued. "He was speedin' along so fast that when he went down, his neck —"

The old man puffed, and the flame rose and fell. *Puff, puff, puff.*

"When he went down, his neck hit the edge of the ice an' that ice was so sharp, it cut his head right off."

"Oh, my!" a lady breathed.

"Told you it warn't goin' to be like nothin' you ever heerd before. Yes, sir! It cut his head right off. Slick as a whistle. His head went a-skiddin' across the ice without pausin' a bit. An' the man's body, under the ice, went right along, too, carried by the speed he was goin' an' by the currents in the water.

"An' then a real curious thing happened." Another match, struck along the bottom of Uncle Ed's chair, broke into flame and was drawn toward the waiting pipe.

"Most curious thing I guess I ever saw, almost. The skiddin' head on the ice an' the body under the ice moved along at the same speed —" He blew the match out. "Moved along at the same speed, an' they come to another hole in the ice jest at the exact same time.

135

The body bobbed up, of course, an' it an' the skiddin' head stuck together. Like I say, it was real cold, an' they jest sort of froze together. By gorry, I never seen such a thing before, an' I wouldn't of believed it if I hadn't bin right there an' seen it m'self with my own eyes.

"I run out on the ice an' pulled the feller out. Seemed like not much was wrong with him 'cept he was as stiff as a frozen fish. I wrapped him up the best I could an' took him to camp. He was cold, I kin tell you. Chilled to the bone. But, like I say, he seemed pretty good, which s'prised me some.

"I got him somethin' warm to eat, an' he told me his name. Frost, it was. That was kind of peculiar, too, warn't it? It bein' so cold an' all. An' d'you know, he didn't want nothin' warm to eat. No, sir. Wouldn't eat it. I thought that was curious, because you always read, an' folks always tell, that when a body is cold, he ought to eat somethin' warm. He was a real pleasant feller. But it seemed he jest couldn't git warm. Fact is, he didn't want to git warm. Stayed sort of over in the corner, as far away from the fireplace as he could git."

"Poor fellow," murmured one of the ladies.

"Yup. Poor feller," the Sage of Beaver Pond agreed. "Like I say, I built up a good fire, but it seemed like he didn't feel like gittin' warm. He set back in the corner shiverin' an' drinkin' some cold water. 'Course it was ice water. I had to break ice in the bucket. It was some cold, I kin tell you.

"But nonetheless we was talkin' some. He told me between his shivers that he always did like to skate, but he guessed mebby he was gittin' a bit too old for it.

"Fin'lly he says he figgered he might like to try to go to sleep, so we turned in. 'Course I wanted to see that he was covered up good. But, no. He didn't want that, an' I noticed that he kep' the covers off of him all night. It was cold, too. A couple of bear skins felt real good to me, I kin tell you.

"Wal, sir, that went on for more'n a week. Day an' night that feller didn't git warm. Didn't want to git warm. It was a real cold snap an' I didn't think I ought to try to move him very far because he was gittin' along all right. I figgered that any man who had an accident like he did ought to be left alone as much as possible.

"But, y'know, he used to go outdoors an' set on a bench that was there beside the door. I didn't for the life of me see how a man could stand so much cold, after all he had been through, but he stood it all right.

"An' d'you know, before long he started to perk up an' started to eat some warm grub an' set up close to the fire. Fin'lly he got all right again an' got hisself thawed out, an' he was jest as good as he ever was. Chipper as could be.

"I was some s'prised when he was able to leave. By

gorry, I never thought such a thing could happen.

"He come back for several years after that. He skated a little, too, but he didn't cut up them fancy didoes any more. An' he come back to see me, too, of course. A feller don't forgit very easy a man who done what I done for him.

"Then he started ailin' an' he wrote to me regular for a couple of years. Then he died. Weak heart, it was. An' d'you know, it's got so you couldn't scarcely see no mark round his neck, which I always thought was curious, seein' what had happened, an' all. No, sir. It healed up jest fine.

"I guess that was 'bout the most curious thing I ever see happen, almost. I always did wonder what might of happened if he'd thawed out too soon. What would of happened if he'd et some warm food like I wanted him to, or set up too close to the fire too soon. I guess the cold, an' the pure water an' the fresh air we got up here was healin' enough to jest naturally heal him up. If he was keerful, that is.

"Another funny thing, too. He used to tell me that he had always had headaches. Suffered from 'em some-thin' fierce. Before the accident, that was. But he never had any headaches after the accident. I never could understand that.

"Yup. I declare, I wouldn't of believed it if I hadn't seen it m'self. Yup. It certainly was a curious thing the way that happened. Real curious, I always thought."

Uncle Ed Tracks a Rabbit

"**D**id you like it out West, Mr. Grant? When you went out there that time?"

It was after dinner and the guests were seated comfortably in the shade on the porch. The sun was warm. A little breeze washed its way across the pond, trickled over the grass and through the shady porch before disappearing into the woods in search of another pond to ripple.

It was the kind of question that could bring forth a story.

"Did I ever tell you 'bout the time I had with a jack rabbit?" Uncle Ed asked.

"When you thought they were lambs? Yes, you did."

"No. I don't mean that time. This was another time. Seems like I had a lot of trouble with jack rabbits. Didn't understand 'em. They warn't nothin' like the rabbits we got here in Maine. I warn't used to 'em.

"Wal, sir, this time I was in a place called Grant's Pass. Least that's what it's called now. There was four of us, an' a big blizzard come up. We couldn't go forward, an' we couldn't go back. Then we run out of grub. Starvation was lookin' us right in the face.

"Seemed like no one was goin' to do anything 'bout it. Two of the fellers was Western men, too. Knowed the country, an' all. 'Course, in a way I don't blame 'em much for not wantin' to git out in that weather. It was sixteen below zero.

"But somebody had to do somethin', an' I jest decided it was me. I made up my mind to go out an' git us somethin' to eat, so I started out from the camp we was in. Not a critter was stirrin'. There warn't none around to stir. I couldn't find no tracks nowhere.

"Jest as I was 'bout to give up, I see what looked like rabbit tracks. Not very clear, though, because the wind was blowin'. It was a big rabbit, too. If I could jest ketch that critter, he might tide us over until the

140

storm stopped. 'Course wherever there is rabbit tracks there has got to be a rabbit at the end of 'em, so I started in to track him down.

"By gorry, it was quite a job, I kin tell you. It was snowin' an' the wind was blowin' somethin' fierce. An' like I say, it was sixteen below. But I kep' on a-goin'.

"The tracks seemed to change once in a while. First it seemed like they was goin' this way, an' then it seemed like they was goin' that way. Wal, now, that's curious, thinks I.

"Then I see what had happened. That was some wind that was blowin', I kin tell you. It was blowin' them tracks around in the snow, first puttin' the tracks of the hind feet first, an' then puttin' the tracks of the front feet first. The result was I didn't know whether I was goin' to where that rabbit was, or whether I was goin' to where he had been. It was a pretty desperate situation. I certainly was glad I was a pretty good tracker.

"I kep' on a-goin' an' the further I went, the more certain I was that I was trackin' that rabbit back to where he had been instead of to where he was goin' to. But, never mind, thinks I. I'd jest as leave be on the trail tryin' to do somethin' as back in camp not tryin' to do anything.

"Anyway, there warn't much else I could do 'cept keep goin'. Them tracks was the only ones I had seen, so I jest kep' on follerin' 'em.

141

"The wind was blowin' so hard it got them tracks mixed up somethin' fierce. First they looked like they was goin' this way, then it seemed like they was goin' that way. I couldn't be goin' back and forth all the time coverin' the same ground, so I jest kep' on follerin' 'em in the same direction I started out.

"Jest as I was 'bout to expire, I come to the end of the tracks. Now there warn't no question 'bout whether the tracks was goin' forward or backward. There warn't no tracks goin' anywhere. They had disappeared.

"All right, thinks I. This is what I was waitin' for. At the end of every rabbit track there is a rabbit. So I started to dig down in the snow, an' there, as snug and cozy as you would want, was three young rabbits. Not little, mind you, but young. Jest right. Seems like the daddy of them rabbits had left the tracks I'd been follerin'. But I had follered 'em backwards, and I had tracked him right back to where he had come from. This was his home.

"I grabbed 'em right quick before they could hop away an' took 'em back to camp. Y'know, a rabbit ain't got much of a chance in deep snow. He can't go very far or very fast, an' a man can ketch a rabbit easy.

"They saved our lives, them three rabbits did. We had rabbit stew until the weather cleared up, an' like I say, there was sure a lot of weather.

"Yup. That was real curious the way the wind shuffled them rabbit tracks 'round so I couldn't tell which way they was pointin'. Good thing I was a pretty good tracker, I guess.

"Ever since then they called the place where that happened Grant's Pass. It's out in Oregon."

Ed Grant Has a Dream

"I had 'bout the strangest dream one night I ever had, an' it settled a problem that had bin botherin' me for some time," remarked Ed Grant.

It seemed as though another tale might be on its way. It was after supper and the Sage of Beaver Pond had an audience. The audience showed the proper interest, for nothing could complete a beautiful Maine

145

day like one of Uncle Ed's stories.

"How was that, Mr. Grant?" asked one of the guests.

"Wal, seein' it's you, I'll tell you. Y'know, ordinarily I wouldn't put too much stock in dreams, but this time I'm tellin' 'bout, I dreamt I died an' went to heaven. An' I figger that any dream 'bout heaven must have somethin' to it. Stands to reason, I should think, wouldn't you?"

"Well, I don't think I ever thought about it before, but it does sound reasonable," was the reply.

"Yup. That's the way I figgered it. Wal, sir, I was guidin' all the time then. That was 'fore I started these camps. There was lots of guides, same as there is now. Some fellers was even sayin' they was guides who didn't hardly know nothin' 'bout it. An' you got to know what you're doin' when you're out guidin'. People dep+endin' on you, an' all.

"Wal, like I say, I dreamt I died an' went to heaven. There was a long line of folks waitin' to git in. They was waitin' to git their new clothes. Y'know, the long white ones. An' then they had to git their wings, an' git them fitted jest right. An' they had to git their harps, an' all that. I kin tell you, before I dreamt it, I never dreamt there was much folderol 'bout gittin' into heaven.

"But, no. 'Twarn't no folderol. There is a lot of details that is necessary to be took keer of. If you stop to think 'bout it, y'kin see that would be the case. By

146

gorry, there you are, without no baggage nor nothin', startin' a whole new life. Or perhaps I should say, startin' a whole new after-life.

"It was a long line, an' I was figgerin' what kind of an instrument I could play, me not bein' very musical. Them harps might be too much for me. But I figgered I might be able to play a mouth harp or a juice harp. I was wonderin' if they'd keep a feller out who couldn't play good enough, but then I figgered, no, they'd have some teachers, prob'ly, to teach 'em.

"Fin'lly, I got up to Saint Peter an' my turn come. He didn't even look at me. Jest' says, 'What's your name?' Kinda businesslike, he was, too.

" 'Ed Grant,' says I.

" 'Residence?' says he.

" 'Rangeley an' thereabouts,' says I.

" 'Oh, yes,' he says, soundin' a little less strict. 'Good fishin' there, wouldn't you say?'

" 'The best,' says I.

" 'It's a strange thing,' he says. 'We put big fish down there. Fish so big you'd think nobody would have to lie 'bout 'em, but do you know, it seems like they still aren't big enough for some people. They still got to lie 'bout 'em. We lost lost of customers up here on account of that.'

"All this time he was goin' through the book, y'know, turnin' pages an' all. 'Oh, yes. Here 'tis,' he says. 'Hmm-m.' He was lookin' real serious now. But

I figgered I hadn't nothin' to worry 'bout, 'count of me always livin' such an honest life.

" 'Occupation?' he asks.

" 'Guide,' says I.

"With that, he says, 'Stand aside. Next.'

"By gorry, I didn't know what to do. 'Course, the next feller was there waitin' in line, an' the rest of 'em was pushin' along. Wal, sir, there was no place for me so I jest wandered over an' set down on a stone."

"Was it a golden stone, Mr. Grant?" someone asked.

"How did y'know?" Uncle Ed replied. "That's jest what it was!" he added explosively. "I noticed it was kind of a yeller stone, an' I looked at it. Never seen one quite like it. It must of bin a second quality one that warn't quite good enough to use for pavin' the streets up there with.

"I jest set there wonderin' what's goin' to happen, 'cause it seemed certain I warn't invited in. An' 'course there ain't many places left to go at that point.

"I could see through the slits in the gate some. The walls was made of yeller stone, too, but 'course they must of bin first quality. Gold, that is. Jest like they say. I could hear the heavenly band practicin', too. Sounded fine. But I was some worried, I kin tell you.

"Fin'lly, I went back an' stood in line agin. When I come to Saint Peter, he looked at me an' he says, kinda firm, 'I thought I told you once to stand aside, please.'

148

"But this time I was a-goin' to find out what was wrong. Here I had spent my whole life bein' truthful, an' I figgered mebby somethin' was wrong. Mistake in the records or somethin'. So I jest spoke up. Gorry, I never was afeerd of bears an' such, so I didn't see that I should be afeerd of Saint Peter either. He'd be understandin' even though he was tired. I could see that he was tired. He's bin meetin' an' talkin' to people for a long time. Must be kinda monotonous askin' the same questions to people all day long, I thinks.

"So, like I say, I jest spoke up. 'Why can't I come in?' I asked.

"Saint Peter says, 'My man, you're a guide, didn't you say?'

" 'Yup,' " says I.

" 'All right,' says he. 'This is heaven. We don't allow *guides* in here.'

"Gorry! There warn't nothin' for me to do but go over to the stone agin an' set down. I was feelin' pretty sorry for m'self. The line was full up. I see people goin' into heaven all the time. Then my eyes popped open. There was Martin Fuller. He was that guide from Dead River. Leastways, he was guidin' people. An' Saint Peter give him the glad hand an' ushered him right through the technicalities an' give him a harp an' a nice pair of shiny wings, an' escorted him through the pearly gates personally.

"Wal, sir, I warn't goin' to stand for that. So I marches right up an' gits in line agin. Fin'lly I gits to Saint Peter an' he looks up. 'See here,' he says, 'I thought I told you there warn't no guides allowed in heaven.'

"Wal, sir, I had him that time, so I come right out an' I says, 'That's what you told me, but then Martin Fuller come up an' he gits in. An' he's a guide.'

"Saint Peter looks at me, an' he says, 'We looked into that real keerful, an' we don't make mistakes up here An' the fact is, he ain't a guide. He only *thinks* he is.'

"After that I woke up an' I started these camps, an' quit bein' a guide. I ain't takin' no chances. I spent my whole life bein' truthful, an' I ain't goin' to be kep' out on 'count of no technicality like that.

"Yup. That was 'bout the strangest dream I ever had. I figgered I ought to pay some attention to it."

The Author

HAROLD W. FELTON, a lawyer by profession, has for many years devoted his leisure time to writing for young people. An intense interest in American folklore led to the first of his widely acclaimed books, an anthology of legends about Paul Bunyan. Since that time he has pursued folk heroes and tall tales with enthusiasm, and his *Pecos Bill: Texas Cowpuncher; John Henry and His Hammer; Fire-Fightin' Mose; Bowleg Bill: Seagoing Cowpuncher; Cowboy Jamboree; New Tall Tales of Pecos Bill*, and *Mike Fink: Best of the Keelboatmen* rank him as a master yarn-spinner.

Born in the Midwest, Mr. Felton now lives in Jackson Heights, New York.

The Artist

LEONARD EVERETT FISHER, whose striking black and white line drawings aptly capture the tongue-in-cheek humor of Ed Grant's Maine tall tales, is the winner of a Pulitzer Art Prize and awards by the American Institue of Graphic Arts. His outstanding illustrations have enhanced numerous books for young readers.

Mr. Fisher and his family reside in Westport, Connecticut.